EAGLE
C·L·A·S·S·I·C·S
FRASER
OF AFRICA

HAWK

★★★ BOOKS

**EAGLE CLASSICS:
FRASER OF AFRICA**

ISBN 0 948248 32 7

Published by
HAWK BOOKS LIMITED
SUITE 309, CANALOT STUDIOS
222 KENSAL ROAD
LONDON W10 5BN
ENGLAND

Fraser of Africa Copyright © 1990 Fleetway Publications
This arrangement Copyright © 1990 Hawk Books Ltd.

Editing & Design: Mike Higgs Graphics

Printed in England

FRANK BELLAMY & FRASER OF AFRICA

by Norman Wright

Frank Bellamy loved the plains and forests of Africa with their abundant and infinitely varied wildlife. He was fascinated by the ancient tribal customs and traditions and became something of an expert on them. As a young boy one of his greatest ambitions was to be a big game hunter and range through the endless grasslands and jungles of the vast continent. He was particularly drawn by the big cats and whenever a circus visited his home town in Kettering he would spend much of his out of school time wandering around the cages, looking at the ferocious felines. As a very small boy of seven or so he approached close enough to pluck a few hairs from the tail of one of the circus lions. He kept his prize for years afterwards safely stored in a bottle! Such a venture required no small measure of courage, for even a sleeping, well fed, caged lion is a daunting target and the act, possibly rather foolhardy, demonstrated something of the sheer determination the lad had.

While serving in the army during the Second World War, Frank volunteered to go to Africa, but his request was turned down. The army was keeping him fully occupied drawing detailed illustrations of anti-tank gun mechanisms and endless aircraft recognition drawings. His superiors told him that they could find plenty of able-bodied men to volunteer for service in Africa, but no one to carry on with the sort of work that he had been producing. He never did get the opportunity to serve in Africa during his time in the army, and most of his knowledge of the flora, fauna and peoples of the continent was gained second hand from reference books and the small collection of African mementoes that he had accumulated since his brush with the circus lion. It is difficult to believe that, despite his great enthusiasm for the 'dark continent', Frank Bellamy only ever visited Africa once, when he and his wife Nancy went on holiday to Morocco. As he stepped off the plane he took a photograph of his foot making that historic first step onto African soil!

Frank's earliest artistic influences were the penny and tuppenny comics of his childhood. Like most youngsters growing up in the 1920's and 1930's he began with "Rainbow", "Chips" and the like, but the rather static style of Tiger Tim and Weary Willie soon lost its appeal. As he journeyed through boyhood he came across the American pulp magazines. Their bright covers were dynamic and exciting and far more to his taste. He also discovered the American Sunday Comic Sections and eagerly read copies borrowed from a friend. He was particularly impressed by "Tarzan" as depicted by Hal Foster, the animals of course being the main attraction. When the strip was later taken over by Burne Hogarth it lost some of its appeal to the young Bellamy. Frank Bellamy never admitted to being influenced directly by any other artist or illustrator, but it is tempting to speculate that thirty years later, when he began to plan his own great African adventure strip, he was subconsciously influenced by those exciting jungle strips he had read as an impressionable young teenager. His work certainly bore the great sense of movement that was a hallmark of Burne Hogarth's strips.

After leaving school, Frank found work in a local studio where he stayed until he was called up for the army. After the Second World War he went back to the same studio for a short time before heading south to London in 1948. He had with him a list of studios that he intended visiting and he hoped that he might find work at one of them. His first port of call was the Norfolk Studios near Fleet Street, and to his surprise he was offered a job straight away.

His knowledge of, and love for the wild life of Africa was put to good use in some of his early work. He drew many illustrations with an African flavour for the "Outspan Magazine", and for "Everybody's Weekly" he produced a drawing of "King Solomon's Mines". The "Boys' Own Paper" for September 1952 carried a splendid full page illustration by Frank Bellamy to go with "Devil Lion", a story by C. T. Stoneham. It depicted Bill

Martin, very much a Fraser of Africa type, being confronted by a huge shaggy maned lion. The green tints that Frank used for the illustration gave it a rich brooding quality. The central figure was beautifully drawn with almost photographic attention to detail. Every fold and crease of his safari jacket hung in such a natural position that the reader could easily have imagined that he was looking through a window out onto a tense jungle scene. The illustration was by far the best thing in that particular issue of "Boys' Own Paper".

Early in 1952 Frank drew his first comic strips. They were fairly crudely drawn, single bank advertisement strips for Gibbs Dentifrice entitled "Commando Gibbs versus Dragon Decay". They began appearing in "Eagle" comic early in 1952 and continued on and off throughout the year. Looking at them today it is difficult to believe that within ten years the same artist would have produced some of the very finest artwork ever to have appeared in a British comic.

Frank stayed with Norfolk Studios until 1953 when he was offered work on "Mickey Mouse Weekly" and decided to go completely freelance. His first job for the comic was "Monty Carstairs" and he took over responsibility for the upper class, monocled investigator on 25th of July 1953 in an adventure entitled "The Secret of the Sands", a tale of smuggling set in Cornwall. The black and white drawing was rather static when compared with much of his later work, but it was a vast improvement on "Commando Gibbs". Later while still working for "Mickey Mouse Weekly" he produced his first full colour comic strip, a spread in the "Living Desert" series, based on one of the Walt Disney true life adventure films. Frank was allowed to sign his "Monty Carstairs" strips, but all of the artwork for the "Living Desert" colour pages had to bear the signature 'Walt Disney'.

Bellamy's long association with Hulton Press started in 1954 when he began drawing "Swiss Family Robinson" for "Swift", a comic aimed at a slightly younger age group than "Eagle". "Swiss Family Robinson" was quickly followed by "King Arthur and His Knights", a strip that clearly demonstrated Frank's skill as a first class adventure strip artist. Towards

King Arthur and his Knights

the end of the serial he drew some powerful battle scenes; frames thronged with armour clad knights on charging horses. It remains one of the best strip versions of the Arthurian legend ever published in a British comic. Arthur finished on 5th May 1956 and was immediately followed by "Robin Hood and His Merry Men", a well drawn strip that continued well into 1957. Robin Hood lacked the pageantry of its predecessor and, having little humour, remained rather darkly brooding.

One of Frank Bellamy's best remembered strips was his pictorial biography of Sir Winston Churchill, entitled "The Happy Warrior", that ran on the back page of "Eagle" from late in 1957 until September 1958. The comic had a long tradition of publishing strip biographies, but up to 1957 they had always been of historical figures. Churchill was the first living personality to have his life story chronicled in such a way within its pages. Marcus Morris, editor of "Eagle", had been very impressed by Frank Bellamy's work in "Swift" and commissioned the artist to undertake the difficult task of drawing Churchill's life story for the comic. Frank found it rather

Commando Gibbs is in every tin of Gibbs, ready to defend your teeth against decay. But you must play *your* part too—you must clean your teeth night and morning with Gibbs. For every time you forget, you give Dragon Decay his chance to attack.

You'll love Gibbs grand flavour too as you *feel* those Gibbs active bubbles getting to work, helping to keep your teeth white and guarded against decay! Red, green and blue cases—so you can always tell your own case of Gibbs by the colour.

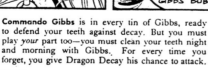

Commando Gibbs is in every tin of Gibbs, ready to help defend your teeth against decay. But you must play *your* part too—you must clean your teeth night and morning with Gibbs. For every time you

forget, you give Dragon Decay his chance to attack.
So let Gibbs active bubbles help keep your teeth white and guarded against decay.
Red, green or blue cases—so you can tell your own.

'Whom neither shape of danger can dismay.
Nor thought of tender happiness betray:
Who, not content that former worth stand fast,
Looks forward, persevering to the last...
And, while the mortal mist is gathering, draws
His breath in confidence of Heaven's applause:
This is THE HAPPY WARRIOR.'

WILLIAM WORDSWORTH

THE FINAL EPISODE OF 'THE HAPPY WARRIOR' WAS THIS
FULL PAGE PORTRAIT OF SIR WINSTON CHURCHILL..
UNFORTUNATELY IT WAS NOT INCLUDED IN THE HULTON
REPRINT BOOK, OR THE MORE RECENT 'DRAGON'S DREAM'
VERSION.

5

THE SHEPHERD KING — The story of DAVID

King Saul's resentment of David, hero of Israel, has reached its climax. Following a warning from Jonathan, the King's son, David is forced to fly to escape death. He seeks refuge in the monastery at Nob, but David's words with the High Priest are overheard by a traitor, who makes a violent dash from the monastery to take the news to Saul . . .

TOLD BY CLIFFORD MAKINS
DRAWN BY FRANK BELLAMY

TREACHERY! STOP HIM!

TOO LATE! HE HAS VANISHED INTO THE NIGHT...

THAT MAN IS DOEG THE EDOMITE—A HERDSMAN OF SAUL'S. DAVID, YOU HAVE BROUGHT DEATH TO THE CITY OF NOB. GO NOW!

DAWN. THE WEARY DAVID PAUSES TO REST...

I MUST FIND A PLACE TO HIDE. I MUST FIND MEN WHO WILL FIGHT FOR ME AGAINST SAUL — OR ISRAEL WILL PERISH.

SUDDENLY...

WHO'S THIS?

HIS FACE IS FAMILIAR...

WHY, IT'S...

I AM DAVID, SON OF JESSE, NOW A FUGITIVE FROM SAUL. I NEED SHELTER AND SUPPORT!

WE ARE NO FRIENDS OF SAUL'S, BELIEVE ME! WE WILL SHOW YOU A PLACE TO HIDE NOT FAR FROM HERE...

David finds refuge in the Cave of Adullam, near the Valley of Elah, and trusty messengers go throughout the land to rally supporters to his cause.

MEANWHILE, SAUL RAGES IN GIBEAH...

DAVID IS PREPARING WAR AGAINST US! YOU HAVE ALL BETRAYED ME — AND YOU, JONATHAN, MY SON, ARE THE WORST OF ALL!

YOU HAVE DONE DAVID A GREAT WRONG!

YOUR MAJESTY! THERE IS A MAN OUTSIDE WHO HAS NEWS OF THE TRAITOR DAVID! HE IS YOUR HERDSMAN, DOEG THE EDOMITE...

TO BE CONTINUED

AN EPISODE FROM THE EXCITING 'SHEPHERD KING' THAT RAN IN 'EAGLE' FROM 1958 - 1959

a daunting job but entered into it with his usual enthusiasm. Great historical accuracy was required and he used a large number of reference photographs, many of which were supplied by the Imperial War Museum. The same museum played host to him on several occasions when he visited it to study weapons and uniforms at first hand. He entered into the work with caution. Early episodes of "The Happy Warrior" were formally laid out, but as the story progressed he began to experiment with layouts, developing a more exciting style that became his hallmark. He introduced large splash panels and irregular shaped frames. Viewed as a whole there is a striking difference between the first six episodes and the final half dozen. The strip was an outstanding success and the enthusiastic response of readers resulted in it being reprinted in book form soon afterwards. Three leather bound copies of the book, printed on special paper, were produced. One was presented to Sir Winston Churchill, one was given to Clifford Makins, who had scripted the strip, and the third was given to Frank Bellamy.

There was no rest for the artist after "The Happy Warrior", he went straight on to draw another full colour historical biography for the back page of "Eagle". This time it was a biblical story, "The Shepherd King - The Story of David". It was a magnificent job; literate, visually splendid and rich in colour. Never before had the story of David received such exciting treatment as it did on those "Eagle" back pages. It contained all the elements that would thrill a young audience - most of all plenty of action and battles! But all too soon it was over, just thirty one episodes that came to an end in February 1959.

For his 'hat trick' on the back page Frank had something rather different; "The Travels of Marco Polo", the story of the thirteenth century merchant adventurer who journeyed to Asia, and ended up spending twenty fours years at the court of the fabulous Kublai Khan. The story got off to a fairly slow start as the background of Marco's early years was explained to readers. It was a few weeks before Frank really got into his stride, but, alas he never finished the story for Odhams Press, the new owners of "Eagle" and all of the other comics formally owned by Hulton Press, persuaded him to take on a job that they considered to be far more important than the back page of "Eagle". The last episode of Marco Polo to be drawn by Frank appeared in "Eagle" dated 6th of June 1959. The rest of Marco's adventures were illustrated by Peter Jackson.

Odhams Press took over Hulton Press in 1959 and, like most 'new brooms', they were determined to make some changes. They considered "Eagle" to be rather dated in appearance and set about

FRANK BELLAMY'S VERSION OF 'DAN DARE'.

bringing it up to date. Their first target was "Dan Dare", Eagle's cover character. The new owners did not like the 'studio system' that Frank Hampson, Dan's creator, had built up to produce the weekly quota of "Dan Dare pages". Their main objection was that it was too costly and had to be brought into line with the production costs of other comic strips. Finding it impossible to work under the new regime imposed by Odhams Press, Hampson's long association with the character ceased, and the publishers had to look around for another artist to take over the character. They had to look no further than the back page of "Eagle" to find a man whose dynamic style would be ideal to depict the exploits of the comic's famous galactic adventurer.

When Frank Bellamy was asked to work on "Dan Dare" his brief was not only to take responsibility for the artwork, but also to make drastic changes in the uniforms and equipment used by Dan Dare and the rest of his Space Fleet team.

Frank carried out his brief splendidly but with slight unease for he preferred to build up his own characters rather than tamper with those created by somebody else. Another disadvantage of working on the "Dan Dare" strip, at least as far as Frank was concerned, was that it was not a one man job. He was assisted by Don Harley and Keith Watson, both former members of Frank Hampson's 'studio' team, a group of artists he had assembled to produce the "Dan Dare" strip using a method very akin to that of a film animation studio, with different members of the team taking responsibility for various aspects of the production. Frank warily agreed to work on "Dan Dare" for a limited period. Things got off to a bad start when, having carried out his instructions and re-vamped the leading characters, he found that his employers got cold feet at the last moment and asked Don Harley to change Bellamy's artwork so that Dan Dare looked more like his old self! Eventually details were sorted out and Frank journeyed up to

London every week to consult with his two assistants. He then returned home to his studio to complete one of the two "Dan Dare" pages while Don Harley and Keith Watson remained in London to produce the second page. It was far from an ideal situation for everyone concerned. Don and Keith had grown used to Frank Hampson's method of production and found it difficult to adapt to the changes. Frank Bellamy, on the other hand, was a loner and preferred to be responsible for the total artistic creation of a strip. Bellamy worked on "Dan Dare" for exactly one year. During that time, and despite all of the difficulties, he produced some stunning pages of artwork. But he was glad when the year was up and he could again work on something of his own artistic creation.

When Frank was offered the chance to work on a new African adventure strip to be titled "Fraser of Africa" it must have come like a breath of fresh air after the trauma of "Dan Dare". Not only was it something new and exciting, but it was also on a subject that was very dear to his heart and into which he could put limitless enthusiasm. "Fraser of Africa" began in "Eagle" in August 1960. It occupied one of the comics four full colour centre pages. Those broad colourful pages had always been coveted and over the years they had presented readers with some of the comics most popular features: "Seth and Shorty", "Tintin", "Riders of the Range", "Luck of the Legion" and the famous centre spread 'cutaway drawings', the best of which were drawn by L. Ashwell Wood. "Fraser of Africa" took over from another long running "Eagle" strip, "Jack O'Lantern", a series of swashbuckling adventures set in nineteenth century England, featuring young Jack Yorke. His adventures began in the comic in January 1955. The scripts were by George Beardmore and the artist responsible for most of his colourful escapades was Robert Ayton, who worked on the strip until late in 1959 when it was taken over, on 28th November, by C. L. Doughty, another expert exponent of the historical adventure strip. Doughty drew the strip until its final episode in "Eagle" dated 30th July 1960, when Jack, after much adventuring, was finally back with his father in their ancestral home. At the bottom of the page readers found the usual blurb promising them something really special the following week:
"Lost Safari" - A Thrilling New Adventure Strip Serial - begins in next weeks "Eagle"!
And for once an editorial blurb was not an exaggeration!

"Lost Safari" was the first of three "Fraser of Africa" adventure strips serialised in "Eagle". The scripts were by George Beardmore, who was probably glad of the chance of shift the location of his stories from nineteenth century England to twentieth century Africa. Readers who

had been familiar with "Eagle" for the two years prior to Fraser would have known from experience that if "The Lost Safari" was anywhere near as good as the artist's previous work for the comic they were in for a treat. Many enthusiasts, knowing of Frank Bellamy's interest in all things African, had assumed that it was Frank himself who suggested the idea of "Fraser of Africa". That was not the case. Frank was approached by a member of the "Eagle" staff and asked if he would be interested in working on the strip. At one time it was suggested that, in view of his knowledge of the subject, he might like to script the serial and produce the artwork. But after discussing the project with Clifford Makins, the Comic's assistant editor, he decided that the combined tasks would probably prove to be too onerous for him. He decided to concentrate on the artwork and leave the scripts in other hands.

"Fraser of Africa" looked very different to any other strip that had ever appeared in the pages of "Eagle". Unlike its predecessor it did not sport an abundance of rainbow coloured hues. Readers who had travelled 'West to Santa Fe' with Jeff Arnold on page nine, and faced a "Night of the Jackal" with Luck of the Legion on pages ten and eleven, must have been brought up rather short when they turned to page twelve. For "Fraser of Africa" was not an adventure bursting with colour. Frank Bellamy had attempted to capture the very feel of the hot scorched African landscape, and to do so he had used a limited palette. In an interview published in the November 1973 issue of "Fantasy International", Bellamy explained his intentions. "... I thought it would be an ideal strip for a monochromatic look, particularly a sepia look, being in sun-drenched, tawny Africa......" When the printers, Eric Bemrose Ltd of Liverpool, were told of his idea they were not impressed and expressed doubts that the results he anticipated could be achieved. Colour photogravure was almost an exact science and artists had to be very wary of the colours and shades they used, as the camera could do disturbing tricks. A faint tinge of the wrong shade of red could end up looking green on the printed page! Not to be outdone, Frank returned to his studio and carried out an extensive series of tests with the colours he hoped to use for the strip. He sent the tests off to Bemrose and awaited the results. He was very pleased when he heard that they were positive and he quickly handed in the report to the editor of "Eagle". He was given the go-ahead to continue the strip using the sepia tints and tones that he had visualised. The browns, yellows and orange of the early episodes captured to perfection the hot, parched, East African landscape and conveyed vividly to readers the scorching heat of the blazing African

sun.

The first story, "The Lost Safari", concerned Martin Fraser's quest for a missing group of hunters consisting of Jeb Brewster, a film star who specialised in 'tough guy' roles, and an experienced white hunter named Robert E. Evans. Fraser, Jim Lloyd, his assistant, and three native boys set out through the little known Kasu district of Tanganyika towards the last known camp site of the missing men. The opening episodes not only introduced readers to a very different use of colour in their comic, but also set the scene, with Fraser and his small band travelling across the plains. They had hardly begun their journey when Jim Lloyd sustained a broken leg after the Land Rover in which the party had been travelling was charged by a rhino. Fraser sent Lloyd back with one of the natives while he continued on foot with M'Kuki, his gun bearer, and Hash the cook. They left the trail and took a short cut towards the last location of the lost safari. It was a wise move on the part of the scriptwriter to find some ploy to dispose of the Land Rover, and force his characters to continue their hunt on foot. It allowed far more scope for the first hand appreciation of the terrain over which Fraser was travelling. Soon danger threatened and Hash found himself being pursued by an angry old rogue buffalo. He was narrowly saved from death by a lone Masai warrior named Ona, whom Fraser was surprised to find so far from his home territory. Ona explained that he too was on the trail of the lost safari, but his motives were far different from Fraser's. He had been humiliated by the arrogant Jeb Brewster and was seeking him in order to gain his revenge. An uneasy alliance was formed between Fraser and Ona as they set off on the track of the missing hunters.

Throughout their journey, Fraser, Ona, M'Kuki and Hash encountered many dangers both from wild animals and from hostile tribesmen, yet the scripts and the illustrations were always restrained and realistic. There was never any feeling that the story was far fetched or 'over the top'. "Eagle" was a weekly that remained very much aware of its multi-purpose role. From the start it had set out to maintain high standards in all it presented to its readers. Marcus Morris, the founder editor, had seen the comic strip as more than just a medium of entertainment. He had appreciated its vast potential for educating readers at the same time as giving them an exciting adventure to follow each week. From the very first issue the comic had presented its readers with a succession of exciting factual strips - "The Great Adventurer" (The story of St Paul) "Louis the Fearless" and many others. "Fraser of Africa", while not depicting the life story of a great figure from history, gave readers an accurate geography lesson. No school text book could ever convey half as much detail to its readers as those picture packed ''Eagle'' pages; and with Frank Bellamy as the artist every detail was accurate. Careful research ensured that all of the wildlife was in its correct location, unlike some strips where the action seemed to change from North Africa to South Africa in seconds. Some comics published 'jungle adventures' that had even more blatant errors. The cheap comics published by the firm of Gerald G. Swan were particularly enthusiastic about jungle strips. ''Jungle Pals'', ''Gara the Jungle Man'', ''Mountain of Jewels'', were typical titles that appeared in Swan publications. They all had one thing in common - a complete lack of authenticity!

In his 1973 interview, Frank Bellamy mentioned some additional help that he had in ensuring the authenticity of the strip. ''.....One reader was a farmer in Kenya, East Africa, who kept up a correspondence with me while I was drawing ''Fraser''. The reason for him writing was to keep tabs on me, to see that I kept all the little things correct. Once I had Fraser fighting a wild boar. Well, I'm not too sure about pigs roaming around East Africa, but that one got through....'' It was not only pigs that were encountered. Buffalo, lions, elephants, vultures, rhino, flamingoes and other creatures were met in abundance during the course of ''The Lost Safari'', and all were beautifully drawn.

One feature of the strip that has contributed to its great appeal is its philosophy of conservation. It was years ahead of its time in its attitudes towards the wild life of the African continent. While characters in 'jungle strips' featured in other comics went around depleting the stocks of big game by quickly despatching with a rifle bullet anything and everything that moved, Martin Fraser continually side stepped, allowing the creatures to flourish. When his group disturbed a leopard he advocated moving away, commenting ''Lucky he wasn't hungry! We'd better leave him in peace - come on.....'' When a rhino was encountered blocking the track they did not resort to guns. ''....The old gentleman himself!...Well I guess he's more scared than we are....'' said Fraser as the group of trackers jumped about and frightened the rhino away. Their generosity was rewarded a few episodes later when the rhino, fed up with the continual interruptions, lost his temper with a gang of murderous poachers who were pursuing Fraser's party. The poachers were sent running and Fraser was able to remove an injured member of his group to safety. It is true that there were times when the strip did depict animals being shot, but it was always made very clear that it was a last resort only used when life was at

stake and there was no alternative.

For the first three months of its run Bellamy kept strictly to his limited sepia colours. From November 1960 he occasionally introduced another colour to give the strip some contrast. The strip dated 19th November, for example, featured a large central panel depicting a group of frightened elephants moving through an area of trees and scrub. Bellamy introduced a blue sky in marked contrast to the dry, yellowish heat haze of the other panels. He repeated the blue sky a fortnight later in another sequence that featured elephants. His drawings of the giants of the plains captured both their power and their anger as they crashed through the scrub in search of their tormentors.

''The Lost Safari'' finished in the last week of January 1961 and led straight into the second story entitled ''The Ivory Poachers''. Fraser and Ona, having discovered the fate of the lost safari at the hands of a gang of ivory poachers led by a brute named Schagen, decided to pursue them in an attempt to bring them to justice. A noticeable feature of the second serial was the use of a wider range of colours. It would be interesting to learn whether it was Frank Bellamy's idea to depart from his original intention of keeping rigidly to a limited number of colours in order to vividly depict the dry African landscape, or whether it was an editorial directive dictated by the reaction of readers. Whatever the reason, ''The Ivory Poachers'', while still retaining its very individual feel for the landscapes it depicted, benefited greatly from the slightly more liberal use of colour.

''The Ivory Poachers'' was a faster paced story than ''The Lost Safari''. There was a greater and more continued conflict between the opposing factions, Fraser on one side and the gang of poachers on the other. Wildlife was still featured in abundance, but more of the strips action was concerned with the tracking down and capture of Schagen and his villainous crew. Throughout the strip Fraser continually emphasised mans protective role towards the wildlife, and the poachers were painted in the blackest possible light; readers were left in no doubt that their only motive for the sickening slaughter that they perpetrated was greed. Fraser was equally scathing of the various traps set by the natives. ''.....An elephant spear-trap, another little dodge of the Waribi. And they must know it's just as illegal as the bush-buck snare!. Well, cut it down.....'' The poachers inevitably received their just deserts. One narrowly escaped becoming hippo fodder and eventually died of his injuries. Another was killed by a leopard. Only the leader, Schagen, totally exhausted after his bid to escape, was captured alive and taken back to stand trial for his many

crimes.

The final Fraser strip, entitled ''The Slavers'', began on 27th May 1961 with Martin Fraser and his gun bearer. M'Kuki, on patrol in the Ngambi Game Reserve. It was not long before they were once more headlong into adventure on the track of Arab slavers who had captured an entire tribe. It was back to the more limited palette for ''The Slavers'', and although most episodes retained at least one frame with a blue sky, Bellamy had, to a great degree, returned to the sepia tones of the first Fraser strip.

Such was the power of Frank Bellamy's visuals that the reader could feel an intimacy with his surroundings as he travelled across the arid landscape with Fraser and M'Bimba on the track of M'Bimba's stolen people. They encountered rapids, hostile tribes and the occasional enraged animal on their quest, yet the quality of the script-writing and artwork was such that the story never deteriorated into a man versus animal romp. It always remained believable, and although Fraser invariably managed to achieve his aims, it was always through his skill and foresight rather than by any great super-human strength. 'The Slavers' came to rather an abrupt end in August 1961. After weeks of tracking through the bush, Fraser, M'Kuki and M'Bimba eventually found the stolen tribe and saved them. The leader of the slavers was taken back to stand trial and M'Bimba took his people home to build new dwellings near the site of their burnt out village. The swift ending, while perhaps not allowing as much action as some readers would have liked, did help to preserve the feel for the African terrain that had been carefully built up over the weeks and which would have been spoilt by too much gun-play at the end.

Throughout all three strips Fraser was portrayed as a man with a great sensitivity to his surroundings. His understanding of the wildlife enabled him to avoid confrontation. He had a sound knowledge of the culture and customs of the East African tribes and most of his meetings with the natives were harmonious. The keynote to every encounter was the mutual respect that Fraser and the tribesmen had for each other. When Ona, the Masai warrior, saved Hash from the rogue buffalo by standing in the path of the enraged animal with only a spear and leather shield for protection Fraser said of him, ''...There's a very brave man, M'Kuki. But then these Masai always are.....''

As the story progressed, Ona gradually began to appreciate Fraser's qualities and later, while the Masai warrior nursed the delirious game warden after he had been mauled by a lion, he soliloquised ''....Why do I, a Masai, nurse the bwana and obey him? It must be because I see that he is an El Moran - a man among men....." Bellamy's knowledge of the African tribal people was clearly demonstrated in his carefully drawn, detailed illustrations that depicted not only the weapons used, but also the variety of costume worn by the various tribes.

There were several splendid studies of Ona and M'Bimba, the two warriors who featured throughout the serials.

"Fraser of Africa" was Frank Bellamy's favourite strip, and many enthusiasts believe that it was his best. There are no giant sized panels that spring immediately to the eye. There are no blazing, multi-coloured frames to beat upon the optic nerves. The quality is far more subtle, almost impressionistic. The reader has to read the strip with care, study the detailed panels and soak up the atmosphere in order to savour the full power of Frank Bellamy's masterwork.

FRANK BELLAMY

FRASER of AFRICA

NAIROBI, Tuesday. JED Brewster, star in many Hollywood 'tough' roles, has now officially been declared missing while on safari in the little-known Kasu district of Tanganyika.

With him was an experienced White Hunter, Robert E. Evans, and it is understood that an expedition has been organized to trace missing men.

The District

STILL NO NEWS OF JED

MARTIN FRASER, KNOWN AS FRASER OF AFRICA, JIM LLOYD HIS ASSISTANT, AND THREE NATIVE BOYS, ARE ON THE TRAIL OF THE LOST SAFARI!

WE SHOULD STRIKE THE KASU RIVER VERY SOON, SIR. HOW NEAR ARE WE TO THE LAST CAMP?

LET'S HAVE A LOOK AT THE MAP.

THE SAFARI WAS LAST HEARD OF THERE, FORTY-FIVE MILES AS THE CROW FLIES.

HOW D'YOU RECKON...?

LOOK OUT! RHINO!

ENGINE'S STALLED, JUMP FOR IT!

THE RHINO'S NOT COMING BACK, AT ALL EVENTS.

BWANA! LLOYD HURT BAD.

JUST MY LUCK—A BROKEN LEG! THAT'S WRECKED EVERYTHING AT THE START!

WHAT ON EARTH DO WE DO NOW, SIR?

JEROGI WILL DRIVE YOU BACK. I'LL TAKE M'KUKI AND HASH, AND WE'LL GO IT ALONE, ON FOOT.

JUST LIKE OLD TIMES, M'KUKI!

FRANK BELLAMY

TO BE CONTINUED

11

'Fraser of Africa' is sent with his assistant, Lloyd, to search for a missing safari up the little-known Kasu river. An encounter with a rhino disables Lloyd, so Fraser continues on foot with his gun-bearer and cook-boy, Hash . . .

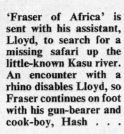

MIGHT BE QUICKER TO LEAVE THE TRAIL, M'KUKI. WE CAN TAKE A MORE DIRECT ROUTE TO THE SAFARI'S LAST CAMP.

QUICKER, BWANA, BUT MORE RISKY.

LATER.

M'KUKI, I'VE GOT AN UNEASY FEELING THAT WE AREN'T ALONE IN THIS VALLEY...

WHAT'S SET THOSE GIRAFFES OFF? I'D SAY THAT WE WERE BEING WATCHED OR FOLLOWED.

MAYBE JUST A LEOPARD, BWANA.

FRASER IS RIGHT!

FRANK BELLAMY

AT LAST THEY REACH THE KASU...

WHITE MAN'S CAMP, BWANA!

THIS COULD BE WHERE THE SAFARI WAS LAST SEEN, M'KUKI. WE'LL PITCH HERE, TOO, BUT LOWER DOWN...

LOOK ROUND FOR CLUES. THE SAFARI WAS MADE UP OF AN AMERICAN FILM-STAR, MY CHUM BOB EVANS, AND FIVE BOYS.

AT ONCE, BWANA!

AMERICANI CIGARETTES, BWANA!

AND HERE'S AN OLD ENVELOPE ADDRESSED TO JED BREWSTER, SO THAT SETTLES IT.

THE QUESTION NOW IS, WHERE DID THEY GO FROM HERE?

THEY GO UP-RIVER FOR SURE, BWANA.

THE COOK-BOY, HASH, WANDERS OFF...

...THEN AN OLD ROGUE BUFFALO CATCHES HIS WIND...

TO BE CONTINUED

Fraser, an African White Hunter, is sent with his gun-bearer and cook-boy to search for a missing safari. They come to the safari's last-known camp, on the Kasu river, where Hash falls foul of a rogue buffalo. The animal charges...

BWANA! BWANA! HE-E-ELP!

SUDDENLY, A SPEAR FLASHES THROUGH THE AIR...

STUNG. THE BUFFALO WHIPS ROUND...

FRANK BELLAMY

AT THE NEARBY CAMP, FRASER IS ALERTED.

THAT WAS A BUFFALO SNORTING. LET'S GO!

HASH IS IN TROUBLE AGAIN!

AM I DREAMING? LOOK AT THAT—A MASAI! A LONE MASAI WARRIOR!

YE GODS, HE'S IN THE WAY—CAN'T GET MY SHOT IN!

BUT THE WARRIOR STEPS ASIDE AND FRASER SEIZES HIS CHANCE.

THERE'S A VERY BRAVE MAN, MKUKI! BUT THEN THESE MASAI ALWAYS ARE...

NOW PERHAPS YOU'LL TELL ME WHAT A MASAI MORAN IS DOING HERE, THREE HUNDRED MILES OUTSIDE HIS TERRITORY?

TO BE CONTINUED

Fraser, an African White Hunter — with his gun-bearer, and cook-boy, Hash — are searching for a missing safari. A lone Masai saves Hash from a rogue bull buffalo . . .

YOU APPEAR FROM NOWHERE, MILES FROM YOUR TRIBE! WHY?

YOU SAVED MY COOK-BOY'S LIFE, SO I DON'T WANT TO MAKE TROUBLE FOR YOU — BUT TELL ME WHY YOU ARE HERE!

BACK IN THE CAMP.

AT LEAST STAY WITH ME — I NEED A GOOD TRACKER. I AM NOT HERE TO HUNT, BUT TO FIND A MISSING SAFARI, AN AMERICANI.

IT IS I, ONA, WHO WILL FIND THE AMERICANI! BUT I AM NO SERVANT. I FIND HIM MYSELF, AND THEN...!

THE MASAI REFUSES TO SAY MORE...

WHAT'S HE DOING NOW, HASH?

SLEEPING, BWANA — HE VERY TIRED MAN.

LIONS ARE AT THE BUFFALO MEAT, BWANA.

KEEP A GOOD FIRE GOING — THEY WON'T HARM US. WHERE'S THE MASAI?

HIM GONE, BWANA — DISAPPEARED!

GONE! WITH ALL THESE CATS ABOUT? WHAT MAKES HIM SO ANXIOUS TO CATCH UP WITH JED BREWSTER?

NEXT MORNING.

WE'LL MAKE FOR THE ELEPHANT POOLS UP RIVER AND, IF WE FIND THE MASAI'S CORPSE, I SHAN'T BE SURPRISED!

YOU HEAR THOSE DRUMS, BWANA?

THEY SAY A STRANGE WARRIOR PASSED THIS WAY, TWO-THREE HOURS AGO!

THEN HE GOT THROUGH ALL RIGHT. WE'LL FOLLOW HIM, AND HE CAN SERVE AS MY TRACKER WHETHER HE LIKES IT OR NOT.

FRANK BELLAMY

TO BE CONTINUED

Martin Fraser, an African White Hunter, is sent with M'Kuki, his gun-bearer, and Hash, the cook-boy, to search for a missing safari. Near the river Kasu, a Masai warrior appears. Fraser discovers that he also wants to find the safari. The stranger disappears, so they follow him . . .

NOW WE CROSS THE RIVER, BWANA?

YES, BUT THIS IS A TRIBAL AREA—WHERE IS EVERYBODY?

THEY ENTER A DESERTED VILLAGE...

FUNNY THING—THEY'VE ALL FLED INTO THE BUSH. WHAT HAVE THEY GOT TO BE AFRAID OF?

THERE'S NOTHING ELSE FOR IT BUT TO BORROW ONE OF THEIR BOATS...

I DON'T KNOW THESE PARTS. KEEP YOUR EYES SKINNED, M'KUKI.

YOU BET, BWANA!

SUDDENLY...

WATCH IT, M'KUKI! EVIDENTLY, WE AREN'T POPULAR! WHAT ON EARTH'S SCARED 'EM?

WE GO DOWNRIVER QUICKLY, BWANA!

CAN'T SAY WE'RE POPULAR WITH THEM, EITHER!

LATER — DOWNRIVER.

FRANK BELLAMY

STAND OFF A BIT, M'KUKI. IT'S A NATURAL WATERING-PLACE, AND YOU NEVER KNOW WHAT'S GOING TO USE IT...

THOUGHT SO! GIVE HIM TIME TO DRINK HIS FILL AND BE OFF.

TWO BOATS BELONGING TO THE TRIBE OPPOSITE— THAT'S INTERESTING! GIVE 'EM A PROPER GOING-OVER, M'KUKI—YOU MAY FIND SOMETHING.

BWANA — QUININE!

TO BE CONTINUED

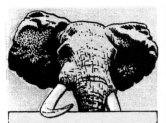

Fraser, an African White Hunter, is sent with his gun-bearer and cook-boy to search for a missing safari. Encountering a lone Masai warrior, who is also tracking down the safari, they follow him. At a river crossing, they find evidence that the safari has passed that way . . .

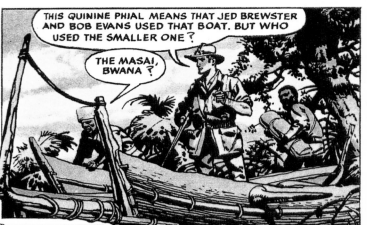

THIS QUININE PHIAL MEANS THAT JED BREWSTER AND BOB EVANS USED THAT BOAT. BUT WHO USED THE SMALLER ONE?

THE MASAI, BWANA?

THEY TAKE UP THE TRAIL, AWAY FROM THE RIVER.

EXACTLY! HE'S HALF A DAY AHEAD OF US, AND THE SAFARI'S ABOUT FOUR DAYS AHEAD OF HIM, SO WE'VE GOT TO HURRY.

BWANA!

WHY ARE YOU AFRAID, MEN OF UKONO, AND WHY DO YOU CARRY SPEARS WHEN THE LAW SAYS THAT ALL SHALL COME AND GO IN PEACE?

OUR CHIEF TELL YOU, BWANA.

THIS MAY BE A STROKE OF LUCK! THE CHIEF OUGHT TO BE ABLE TO TELL US WHAT'S HAPPENED TO THE SAFARI.

FRASER HOLDS A PALAVER WITH THE CHIEF.

ONE PARTY WHITE MEN COME FROM EAST, ANOTHER FROM WEST. THEN AN ARMED WARRIOR, THEN YOU, BWANA.

O BWANA FRASER, WE LEAVE OUR VILLAGE BECAUSE WE ARE AFRAID!

FRANK BELLAMY.

WHAT NONSENSE IS THIS, O M'GULUGULU? I SEEK ONLY ONE PARTY OF WHITE MEN, THE AMERICANI AND BWANA EVANS, WHOM YOU KNOW. TELL ME WHERE THEY CAMP AND YOU WILL TRULY BE WISEST AMONG THE UKONO!

WHITE MEN QUARREL, O BWANA FRASER! WE TAKE OUR CHILDREN TO THE FOREST AND SEE NOTHING, HEAR NOTHING, KNOW NOTHING. IN THIS WAY I AM WISE.

FRASER TAKES THE TRAIL AGAIN.

LATER . . .

STOP! DON'T MOVE! A TUSKER IN A TOWERING RAGE — WHY?

TO BE CONTINUED

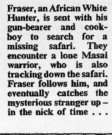

Fraser, an African White Hunter, is sent with his gun-bearer and cook-boy to search for a missing safari. They encounter a lone Masai warrior, who is also tracking down the safari. Fraser follows him, and eventually catches the mysterious stranger up — in the nick of time . . .

GIVE ME THE DOUBLE-EXPRESS, M'KUKI—I'LL HAVE TO DRAW HIS ATTENTION AND KILL HIM! D'YOU SEE WHAT'S LYING AT HIS FEET?

THE MASAI WARRIOR —ONA!

HE'S SEEN ME —THIS IS IT!

FRASER FIRES HIS FIRST BARREL AT THE ONRUSHING ELEPHANT...

...THEN HIS SECOND.

SURELY THIS IS THE FATHER OF ALL ELEPHANTS, WHO FEELS NO BULLETS!

BWANA, BWANA—HE-ELP!

TWO SHOTS IN HIM AND STILL HE'S ALIVE! HE MUST DIE —HE MUST!

THERE HE GOES AT LAST! HE MAY BE A ROGUE— BUT WHAT SPIRIT!

FRANK BELLAMY.

LET'S SEE IF THE MASAI HAS BREATH ENOUGH LEFT IN HIM TO TELL ME WHAT HE KNOWS OF THE MISSING SAFARI!...

TO BE CONTINUED

Fraser, an African White Hunter, is sent — with his gun-bearer and cook-boy — to search for a missing safari led by an American film-star, Jed Brewster. A lone Masai warrior is also tracking the safari, and Fraser rescues him from a rogue elephant...

SO HE'S COMING TO, AT LAST! NO SIGN OF DAMAGE—KNOCKED FLAT AND WINDED, I GUESS

HO, BWANA!

SEE, AN OLD WOUND— BULLET STILL IN HIM!

NO WONDER THE OLD FELLOW WAS SO BAD TEMPERED! BUT WHOSE BULLET? THE MISSING AMERICAN'S?

HE'D NO BUSINESS TO LEAVE A WOUNDED BULL WITHOUT FINISHING HIM OFF!

AMERICAN VERY BAD HUNTER - VERY BAD MAN

SO YOU KNOW THE AMERICANI! WHY IN HEAVEN'S NAME ARE YOU FOLLOWING HIM?

TO KILL HIM!

AND GET YOURSELF HANGED? ONCE AND FOR ALL, ONA, TELL ME WHAT A MASAI IS DOING HERE, MILES FROM HIS TRIBE!

I TELL YOU, O FRASER, BECAUSE YOU SAVED MY LIFE...

WE ARE ON A LION HUNT. I WANT HIS MANE FOR A HEAD-DRES SO I MUST KILL HIM MYSEL THIS AMERICANI COME TO WATCH US...

...THE LION LEAP AT ME. I TAKE IT ON MY SHIELD BEFORE STABBING IT, WHEN — BANG! THE AMERICANI SHOOT...

FRANK BELLAM

...HE SHOOT BECAUSE HE DARE NOT HUNT THE LION ALONE. HE LAUGH AT ME. MY PEOPLE LAUGH. I AM FOREVER SHAMED, SO I TRACK HIM TO KILL HIM.

YOU CANNOT KILL THE AMERICANI, ONA. HE IS A VERY FAMOUS MAN, WHICH IS WHY I LOOK FOR HIM. WILL YOU COME WITH ME AS MY TRACKER?

I WILL BE YOUR TRACKER, O FRASER— AFTERWARDS IS MY AFFAIR.

BWANA! THE MEN OF THE UKONO COME TO CARVE UP THE ELEPHANT AND TAKE THE TUSKS!

TO BE CONTINUED

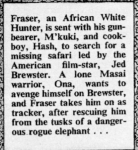

Fraser, an African White Hunter, is sent with his gun-bearer, M'kuki, and cookboy, Hash, to search for a missing safari led by the American film-star, Jed Brewster. A lone Masai warrior, Ona, wants to avenge himself on Brewster, and Fraser takes him on as tracker, after rescuing him from the tusks of a dangerous rogue elephant . . .

WHILE YOU TALK, BWANA, THE FOREST MEN COME WITH KNIVES TO TAKE THE ELEPHANT'S MEAT!

TELL THEIR HEADMAN TO COME TO ME.

GREETINGS, O BWANA FRASER!

GREETINGS, O MAN OF THE UKONO!

THAT PATH, BWANA, TO THE ELEPHANT POOLS ON THE KASU RIVER.

JUST AS I THOUGHT.

YOUR PEOPLE MAY HAVE THE MEAT, BUT YOU ARE TO KEEP THE TUSKS FOR ME. IN RETURN, TELL ME WHICH PATH THE AMERICANI TOOK WITH HIS SAFARI — THE TRUTH!

HE LIES — THE SAFARI WENT INTO THE HILLS.

HOW FAR AHEAD IS THE MISSING SAFARI, ONA?

THERE ARE NO SIGNS, O BWANA FRASER. I SAY THE SAFARI DID NOT GO THIS WAY!

BUT FRASER OVERRULES HIS MASAI TRACKER, AND THEY MAKE FOR THE POOLS.

FRANK BELLAMY

LATE AFTERNOON.

THE POOLS, BWANA!

AND ABOUT TIME! WE'RE ALL PRETTY FLOGGED...

AS PEACEFUL A SCENE AS ANY IN AFRICA! NOBODY'S BEEN HERE FOR WEEKS, CERTAINLY NOT A HUNTING SAFARI. I WAS WRONG, ONA.

WHY DID THE UKONO DELIBERATELY SEND US ON THE WRONG TRAIL? WHAT ARE THEY HIDING?

TO BE CONTINUED

Fraser, an African White Hunter, with his gun-bearer, M'Kuki, and cook-boy, Hash, is searching for a missing safari led by the American film-star, Jed Brewster. Ona, who wants to avenge himself on Brewster, is acting as tracker. Against his advice, they take the wrong trail, but Ona soon puts them right . . .

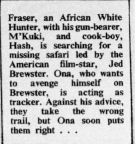

RIGHT—WE'LL TAKE YOUR PATH TO THE HILLS, ONA. ALL THE SAME, IT SEEMS UNLIKELY TO ME THAT THEY'D GO THAT WAY.

SUDDENLY . . .

BWANA!

TAKE MY GUN, M'KUKI, BUT KEEP IT HANDY—THEY'RE THE WARIBI! NOBODY KNOWS MUCH ABOUT THEM, BUT I BELIEVE THEY'RE A PRETTY TRICKY CROWD . . .

MEN OF THE WARIBI! WHY DO SUCH WARRIORS AS YOU COME WITH SPEARS AGAINST AN UNARMED MAN?

CAN YOU UNDERSTAND THEM, M'KUKI, OR YOU, ONA? THEY DON'T SPEAK SWAHILI.

HEADMAN SAY POWERFUL JU-JU MAKE SO WE GO NO FURTHER, BWANA—JU-JU TELL HIM STOP US.

IT DOES, DOES IT! YOU TELL HIM WHITE MAN HAS STRONGER JU-JU.

FRANK BELLAMY

HE SAY HIS JU-JU MOST STRONG OFF ALL, BWANA!

ALL RIGHT— HE'S ASKED FOR I TELL HIM WHITE M. TAKE HIMSELF TO PIECES . . .

SEE, MEN OF THE WARIBI! FIRST, I TAKE OUT MY TEETH, WHICH ARE OF PURE GOLD . . .

THE WARIBI DON'T WAIT FOR MORE, BUT VANISH, TERRIFIED . . .

NO NEED TO TELL 'EM I WAS KICKED IN THE FACE BY A MULE IN '48, AND HAD THREE TEETH REPLACED BY A NAIROBI DENTIST!

SO FRASER ONCE MORE FOLLOWS THE ELEPHANT-TRAIL INTO THE TREES . . .

WHAT WAS THE REAL REASON THEY TRIED TO STOP US? DID THEY AMBUSH THE MISSING SAFARI, FOR INSTANCE — AND, IF SO, WHAT HAPPENED TO IT?

TO BE CONTINUED

Fraser, an African White Hunter, is sent to search for a missing safari led by the American film-star, Jed Brewster. Fraser's Masai tracker, Ona, strikes into the hills, where the superstitious Waribi tribe try to stop them. Fraser, however, puts them to flight . . .

A BUSHBUCK! THE WARIBI HAVE BEEN SETTING SNARES,—PERHAPS THAT'S WHY THEY WANTED TO STOP US. CUT THE BEAST FREE, M'KUKI.

BUT SUPPOSING THE WARIBI AMBUSHED THE MISSING SAFARI? EVEN SO, THEY COULDN'T HAVE KILLED EVERY MEMBER OF THE PARTY...

AN ELEPHANT SPEAR-TRAP— ANOTHER LITTLE DODGE OF THE WARIBI! AND THEY MUST KNOW IT'S JUST AS ILLEGAL AS THE BUSHBUCK SNARE! WELL, CUT IT DOWN!

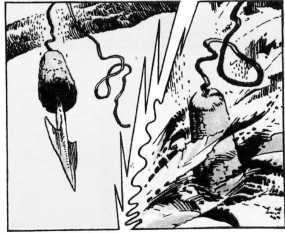

LATER...

BWANA! THE SAFARI—I FIND TRAIL!

SO THE WARIBI DIDN'T WIPE THEM OUT!

ONA FOLLOWS THE TRAIL LIKE A BLOODHOUND.

FRANK BELLAMY

LOOK, BWANA! HERE!

STONE-AGE PAINTINGS!

WHAT ELSE DOES BWANA SEE?

JED.BREW

TO BE CONTINUED

21

FRASER of AFRICA

Fraser, an African White Hunter, is searching for a missing safari led by a Holly-wood star, Jed Brewster. Fraser's Masai tracker, Ona, at last finds convincing evidence that Brewster has struck away from the usual safari trail . . .

STONE-AGE PAINTINGS! BUT WHY DID BREWSTER BREAK OFF CARVING HIS NAME UNDER THEM?

NOW I KNOW WHY THEY CAME THIS WAY. I GUESS THEY HEARD SOME RUMOUR ABOUT THESE PAINTINGS BEING HERE AND CAME TO FIND THEM.

WHAT'S THE MATTER WITH HASH, M'KUKI?

HIM SAY THIS PLACE FULL OF GHOSTS, BWANA. HIM VERY STUPID SOMALI BOY.

COME ON! SEE WHAT ELSE YOU CAN FIND, ONA.

STILL MORE FINDS — THE RUINS OF A STONE-BUILT CITY! NO WONDER BREWSTER'S SAFARI GOT DELAYED!

BWANA SEE WHERE WHITE MAN STRIKE MATCH...

BWANA SEE OTHER THINGS, BAD THINGS!

MY HEAVENS — A GRAVE, NOT THREE DAYS OLD! BUT WHOSE?

FRANK BELLAMY

HASH IS NOT SUCH A STUPID SOMALI BOY AFTER ALL, M'KUKI — BUT WHICH OF THEM DIED, AND WHY?

BWANA — OH, BWANA, LOOK!

FILL A SECOND ONE!

A MAN-KILLER! THE BEGGAR THAT FILLED ONE GRAVE AND WANTS TO...

TO BE CONTINUED

22

FRASER of AFRICA  LOST SAFARI

Fraser, an African White Hunter, is sent to search for a missing safari led by a Hollywood star, Jed Brewster. Fraser's Masai tracker, Ona, leads them to a forest where, amid ancient ruins, they find a new grave. Fraser has no time to wonder whose grave it is, because . . .

THE MASAI IS PROUD, AND FRASER MUST USE ALL HIS TACT.

WITH SWORD AND SPEAR? ONA, THIS IS AN OLD AND TOOTHLESS LION, NOT WORTHY OF A MASAI. WE MUST ALL HUNT HIM...

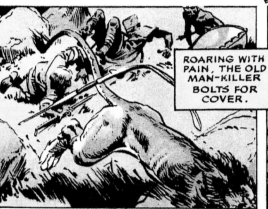

ROARING WITH PAIN, THE OLD MAN-KILLER BOLTS FOR COVER.

I MUST GET HIM— QUICK! WE CAN'T LEAVE A WOUNDED LION RAGING AROUND.

BWANA, I GO KILL HIM— HIM MY LION!

SPREAD OUT AND SIGNAL WHEN YOU SEE HIM — BUT THIS WON'T BE EASY!

TRICKY— CAN'T SEE VERY FAR AHEAD...

ONA'S YONDER. CAN'T SEE M'KUKI. BETTER CALL THEM OFF — TOO DANGEROUS...

FRANK BELLAMY

TOO LATE ...

...IT'S ME HE'S AFTER !

TO BE CONTINUED

23

Fraser, an African White Hunter, is sent to search for a missing safari led by a Hollywood star, Jed Brewster. Fraser's Masai tracker, Ona, leads them to a forest where, amid ancient ruins, they find a new grave. But whose? Then, as a man-killing lion attacks Fraser, he fires . . .

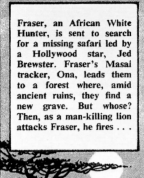

HE'S DEAD! LIFT HIM OFF — I BELIEVE ONE OF MY LEGS IS HURT...

GET MY FIRST-AID PACK, M'KUKI...

HE'S CLAWED ME A BIT, BUT I DON'T THINK IT'S TOO BAD.

SEE THOSE TEETH? WORN DOWN TO THE GUMS. HE'S AN OUTCAST, WHO FOUND WHAT PREY HE COULD AMONG THE RUINS. I DON'T DOUBT HE KILLED ONE OF BREWSTER'S MEN — BUT WHICH?

PERHAPS THE BWANA HIMSELF!

WE'LL CAMP HERE — MUST GIVE THIS LEG A REST UNTIL MORNING.

FRANK BELLAMY

BUT, LATE THAT NIGHT...

M'KUKI — WAKE UP! WHAT'S GOING ON OUT THERE?

I'M HANGED! IT'S THE MASAI, DOING A WAR-DANCE ROUND THE DEAD LION!

NOT WAR-DANCE, BWANA — DANCE OF VENGEANCE!

DOES A MASAI MAKE WAR UPON A DEAD LION, ONA?

WILL THE BWANA TRY TO TAKE MY VENGEANCE FROM ME?

AS THOUGH IN A TRANCE, THE MASAI REPEATEDLY LUNGES AT THE DEAD LION.

NOT SO, BWANA. THE LION IS MY ENEMY, THE AMERICANI! WHEN I FIND HIM, I STAB HIM — SO! — BECAUSE OF THE WRONG HE DID ME.

NO! YOU CAN'T GO TREATING ONE OF THE WORLD'S FILM IDOLS AS THOUGH HE WERE A LION!

TO BE CONTINUED

FRASER of AFRICA  LOST SAFARI

Fraser, an African White Hunter, is in unexplored country, tracking a missing safari led by a famous Hollywood star, Jed Brewster. Fraser shoots a man-killing lion and, that night, finds Ona – his Masai tracker – dancing round the body of the dead animal, pretending that it is that of Brewster . . .

ONA, YOU CANNOT KILL THE AMERICANI AS I KILLED THAT LION!

THE AMERICANI ROBBED ME OF MY HONOUR. THEREFORE, I KILL HIM!

I GIVE YOU YOUR HONOUR BACK, ONA, FOR I KNOW HOW BRAVE YOU ARE. PERHAPS, ALSO, THE AMERICANI LIES IN THE GRAVE WE FOUND. NOW LET US SLEEP.

BUT, AT DAWN...

THE MASAI BWANA – HE GO OFF AGAIN, ALONE!

I THOUGHT HE MIGHT. WE MUST CATCH HIM. HEAVEN KNOWS WHAT'LL HAPPEN IF HE REACHES BREWSTER FIRST!

LATER...

OUCH – THIS LEG OF MINE THROBS WHERE THE LION TORE IT! I HOPE TO GOODNESS THERE'S NO INFECTION.

BWANA, HEAR SOMETHING.

SOUNDS LIKE PIGS SQUEALING. LET'S GO AND INVESTIGATE.

BUSH-PIGS! ONA NEVER FAILS TO FIND TROUBLE.

I DON'T LIKE THE LOOK OF THAT BIG BOAR – HE'S IN A NASTY MOOD.

FRANK BELLAMY

HASH – M'KUKI – STOP GRINNING! YOU KNOW HOW TOUCHY THESE MASAI ARE!

ONA! THE ODDS ARE AGAINST YOU – YOU CANNOT FIND BREWSTER ALONE. NOW COME WITH US – BUT NO MORE TALK OF KILLING!

TO BE CONTINUED

25

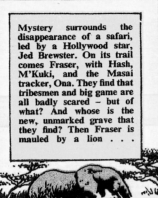

Mystery surrounds the disappearance of a safari, led by a Hollywood star, Jed Brewster. On its trail comes Fraser, with Hash, M'Kuki, and the Masai tracker, Ona. They find that tribesmen and big game are all badly scared – but of what? And whose is the new, unmarked grave that they find? Then Fraser is mauled by a lion . . .

IT'S NO USE, M'KUKI! YOU'LL—HAVE TO—TO PITCH CAMP. NO, NOT HERE — NOT SO CLOSE TO THE ELEPHANT-TRAIL—BECAUSE...

...BECAUSE...

LATER... BWANA IN BAD FEVER, ONA. WILL YOU KEEP WATCH NOW, WHILE I...

I AM NOT THE BWANA'S SERVANT!

THE BWANA SAVE YOU FROM ROGUE ELEPHANT—NOW YOU DESERT HIM. IS THAT THE WAY OF A MASAI?

IS IT THE WAY OF THE ASKARI TO WAG THEIR TONGUES? I WILL RETURN.

DELIRIUM OVERTAKES FRASER...

NOT THERE, M'KUKI! THE ELEPHANTS ARE ON THE MOVE! IF YOU PITCH CAMP THERE, THEY'LL...

NO! BWANA KEEP SILENT—QUITE SILENT, BECAUSE...

THE ELEPHANTS ARE ON THE MOVE!

THE OTHER SIDE OF THE ELEPHANT-TRAIL...

ELEPHANT VERY FRIGHTENED. I MUST MAKE THE BWANA WELL AGAIN, SO HE FIND OUT WHY THE 'TEMBO' ARE FRIGHTENED.

FRANK BELLAMY,

ONA RETURNS TO CAMP...

WHY DO YOU TEAR OFF THE DRESSINGS FROM THE BWANA'S LION-WOUND? DO YOU TRY TO KILL HIM?

AMONG MY TRIBE ARE WISE HEALERS WHO TEACH ME, O TALKATIVE ONE. THIS IS THE FLESH OF CRICKETS THAT I RUB ON HIS WOUNDS...

...AND THIS ROOT WILL BRING OUT HIS FEVER IN MUCH, MUCH SWEAT...

ONA IS RIGHT. AT SUNDOWN, FRASER IS SLEEPING PEACEFULLY.

WHY DO I, A MASAI, NURSE THE BWANA AND OBEY HIM? IT MUST BE BECAUSE I SEE THAT HE IS AN EL MORAN—A MAN AMONG MEN!

TO BE CONTINUED

FRASER of AFRICA

LOST SAFARI

Mystery surrounds the disappearance of a safari led by a Hollywood star, Jed Brewster. On its trail comes Fraser, with Hash, M'Kuki and the Masai tracker, Ona. They find a new grave – whose is it? And what has scared the tribesmen and big game? Fraser is wounded by a lion, and Ona cures his injuries and fever with native remedies . . .

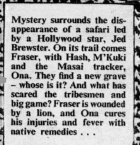

BWANA IS STILL WEAK?

LEGS ARE A BIT GROGGY, THAT'S ALL, BUT I CAN STAGGER ALONG – WE CAN'T AFFORD TO WASTE A DAY RESTING...

WE'VE GOT TO FIND WHERE THOSE FAMILIES OF ELEPHANTS ARE COMING FROM, AND WHAT'S SCARING 'EM. I'LL BET BREWSTER'S SAFARI HAS SOMETHING TO DO WITH IT!

THIS IS A BIT OF A PULL...

SOON WE COME TO THE TOP, BWANA!

MY HAT – I NEVER EXPECTED THIS! IT MUST BE AN OFF-SHOOT OF THE GREAT RIFT VALLEY.

BWANA – SEE OVER THERE!

VULTURES!

WHAT'S GOING ON? SMOKE – AND I CAN JUST SEE FIGURES. MUST BE EIGHT OF THEM ...AND – YES, LOOKS LIKE ELEPHANT CARCASSES...

MUST FIND A WAY DOWN, SOMEHOW – WE'VE GOT TO MOVE FAST!

BUT, TRAVELLING SWIFTLY TOWARDS THEM...

DROP EVERYTHING AND SCATTER!

FRANK BELLAMY.

TO BE CONTINUED

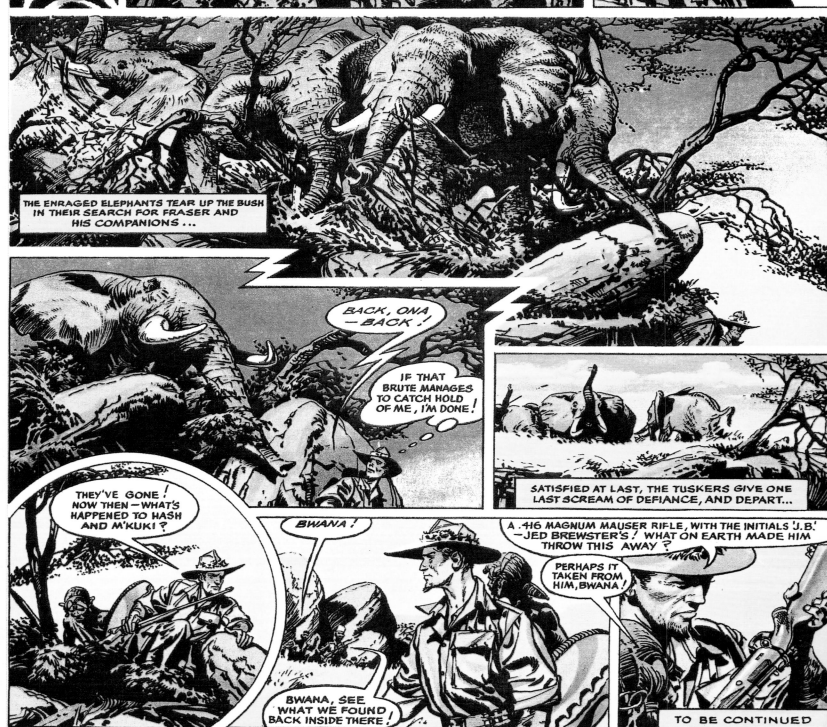

TO BE CONTINUED

FRASER of AFRICA  LOST SAFARI

Mystery surrounds the disappearance of a safari led by Hollywood star Jed Brewster. On its trail comes Fraser, with Hash, M'Kuki and the Masai tracker, Ona. They find a new grave — whose is it? And what has scared the elephants into migration? A herd scatters Fraser's party, and M'Kuki stumbles on another mystery . . .

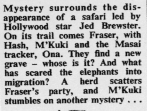

JED BREWSTER MUST HAVE VALUED THIS RIFLE — YET HERE IT IS, THROWN AWAY! HOW LONG HAS IT LAIN HERE, ONA?

ANTS BEGIN TO EAT WOOD, BWANA — HYENA SMELL . . . I THINK IT DROPPED EARLY MORNING, DAY BEFORE YESTERDAY.

TWO DAYS AGO! WE'RE GETTING WARMER — LET'S GET CRACKING . . .

WE'VE GOT TO FIND A WAY INTO THAT GORGE.

WE CAN GO DOWN SAME WAY ELEPHANTS CAME UP, BWANA.

WHAT IS GOING ON DOWN THERE?

VULTURES BY THE DOZEN, AND A LARGE PILLAR OF SMOKE — PERHAPS BREWSTER'S STILL ALIVE DOWN THERE . . .

BUT CAN HE BE ALIVE? HOW DID HIS RIFLE COME TO BE THROWN INTO THAT CAVE BACK THERE? WHAT DID THE UKONO CHIEF MEAN BY 'WHITE MEN QUARRELLING'? WHY IS THE GAME SO CONFOUNDEDLY SCARED?

AN OLD LANDSLIDE — AND THE ELEPHANTS FOUND A WAY UP IT! BUT JUST LOOK AT THE GAME THAT CAN'T MAKE IT AND FIND THEMSELVES TRAPPED!

HOLLYWOOD OR NO HOLLYWOOD, I'LL PUT THE FELLOW IN THE DOCK IF I FIND THAT HE'S RESPONSIBLE!

BWANA, BWANA!

SEE, BWANA — ANOTHER TRAIL! ONE — TWO — THREE WHITE MEN AND MANY BOYS CAME THIS WAY TWO DAYS AGO!

A SECOND SAFARI!

.TO BE CONTINUED

Mystery surrounds the disappearance of a safari led by Hollywood star Jed Brewster. On its trail comes Fraser, with Hash, M'Kuki and the Masai tracker, Ona. When elephants scatter them, Fraser has a narrow escape. Then Ona discovers the trail of a *second* safari, which is led by three white men . . .

BWANA, LISTEN — HYENAS!

YOU'RE RIGHT! LET'S FOLLOW BACK ALONG THIS OTHER SAFARI'S TRAIL...

FOR HEAVEN'S SAKE HURRY! IF THERE'S BEEN TROUBLE, WE DON'T KNOW WHAT WE MAY FIND...

BE OFF, YOU BRUTES!

SEE THAT? THE CARCASSES OF THREE ELEPHANTS WITH THEIR TUSKS GONE — BUT BREWSTER CAN'T HAVE SHOT THEM, BECAUSE HE HAD NO GUN, SO...

BREWSTER NO SHOOT THEM, BWANA — I SHOW YOU WHAT HAPPEN...

FROM LITTLE TELL-TALE SIGNS, ONA RECONSTRUCTS THE CRIME...

THREE WHITE MEN COME THIS WAY. HERE THEY WATCH THE ELEPHANTS FEED — THEN ONE GO THIS WAY, ONE GO THAT. THIRD MAN, HE STAY HERE...

... EACH PICK HIS ELEPHANT AND SHOOT. THE TUSKERS RUN A LITTLE, THEN DIE. THE OTHER ELEPHANTS RUN AWAY. SEE THEIR TRACKS, BWANA?

FRANK BELLAMY.

BY HEAVENS, NOW I UNDERSTAND — POACHERS! BREWSTER AND BOB EVANS RAN ACROSS A GANG OF POACHERS WHAT ELSE, ONA?

THE AMERICANI AND BWANA EVANSI RUN TOWARDS THE KILLING. SEE — THEIR FOOTPRINTS ARE FAR APART...

MANY, MANY, FOOTPRINTS, BWANA, ALL MIXED UP. MEN FIGHT, I THINK...

SEE, A TRAIL OF BLOOD...

AH!

A BULLET-SCAR! SOMEONE PULLED THE TRIGGER OF AN ELEPHANT-GUN...

AND IT WASN'T POINTED AT AN ELEPHANT THIS TIME!

TO BE CONTINUED

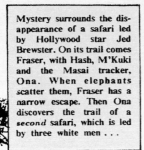

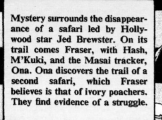

Mystery surrounds the disappearance of a safari led by Hollywood star Jed Brewster. On its trail comes Fraser, with Hash, M'Kuki, and the Masai tracker, Ona. Ona discovers the trail of a second safari, which Fraser believes is that of ivory poachers. They find evidence of a struggle.

A MAN LIE HERE, BWANA— HE BLEED A LITTLE.

NO WONDER BREWSTER'S SAFARI GOT LOST! I RECKON HE MUST HAVE FALLEN FOUL OF SOME POACHERS...

THINGS ARE BEGINNING TO ADD UP — BREWSTER AND BOB EVANS HEARD THE SHOTS, CAME RUNNING...

...AND FOUND THEMSELVES FACE TO FACE WITH THE POACHERS!

A TRACK LEADS HERE, BWANA! IT IS WHERE WE FIND THE AMERICANI'S RIFLE. THE BAD MEN THREW IT THERE TO HIDE IT!

SO THAT'S IT! I IMAGINE THAT EVANS WAS WOUNDED, BUT BREWSTER MADE A FIGHT OF IT AND GOT KNOCKED ON THE HEAD. THE POACHERS THREW HIS RIFLE AWAY, AND THEN...

...MADE OFF WITH BREWSTER AND EVANS AS PRISONERS! LET'S GET AFTER 'EM, BEFORE WORSE HAPPENS!

WE'RE FOLLOWING THE ELEPHANTS' ESCAPE-ROUTE — LET'S HOPE WE DON'T MEET ANY JUST HERE!

AND THERE'S THE GAME THAT CAN'T CLIMB, AND THEREFORE CAN'T ESCAPE FROM THE POACHERS!

LATER...

LOOKS LIKE A CAMP-FIRE, WAY OVER THERE—IT MUST BE THE POACHERS! DARE WE RISK A NIGHT-MARCH?

TO BE CONTINUED

31

Mystery surrounds the disappearance of a safari led by Hollywood star Jed Brewster. On its trail comes Fraser, with Hash, M'Kuki, and the Masai tracker, Ona. They find evidence that Brewster and his White Hunter, Evans, have been overpowered by ivory poachers. Fraser decides to follow the trail into a deep gorge . . .

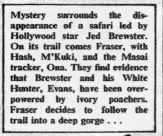

BETTER NOT RISK CREEPING UP ON THEM BY NIGHT—IT'S UNKNOWN COUNTRY TO ME...

THERE'S NO TIME TO SET UP CAMP—LET'S SEE IF THIS CAVE WILL SUIT US...

POOH! SMELLS LIKE...

...LEOPARD!

FRANK BELLAMY.

LUCKY HE WASN'T HUNGRY! WE'D BETTER LEAVE HIM IN PEACE—COME ON...

THEY FIND A SHALLOW CAVE.

THIS PLACE WILL DO.

IN THE ABSENCE OF A FIRE, A WATCH MUST BE KEPT AGAINST PROWLERS.

DAREN'T TELL THE OTHERS WE'RE REALLY UP AGAINST IT. I MUST GET EVANS AND BREWSTER AWAY, BUT THE POACHERS OUTNUMBER US...

WISH I COULD TRUST ONA—HE'S A REAL SAVAGE AT HEART. STILL, I THINK HE'S BEGINNING TO TRUST ME.

AT FIRST LIGHT...

WHERE THE DEVIL HAS ONA GOT TO? IT'S HIS WATCH. HIS SHIELD'S THERE BUT...

NOW WE CAN EAT—THEN WE HUNT THE POACHERS.

THE ONLY THING IN OUR FAVOUR IS THAT THEY'RE NOT EXPECTING US. THEY'RE OBVIOUSLY TOUGH CUSTOMERS, SO WE MUST GET BREWSTER AND EVANS AWAY AS QUICKLY AS WE CAN...

FROM THIS POINT ON, NOT A SOUND! ON YOU GO, ONA!

TO BE CONTINUED

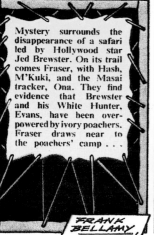

Mystery surrounds the disappearance of a safari led by Hollywood star Jed Brewster. On its trail comes Fraser, with Hash, M'Kuki, and the Masai tracker, Ona. They find evidence that Brewster and his White Hunter, Evans, have been overpowered by ivory poachers. Fraser draws near to the poachers' camp...

FRANK BELLAMY

YOU SEE WHAT THEY ARE UP TO, BWANA?

THEY'VE COLLECTED THE IVORY, READY TO MOVE AND, BECAUSE OF THE LONG TREK AHEAD OF THEM, THEY'VE BEEN PREPARING BILTONG BY DRYING ANTELOPE MEAT...

I SEE BWANA.

NOW WHICH WAY ARE THEY GOING? BACK HERE? CAN'T SEE ANY BOATS TO TAKE THEM BY WATER.

BWANA! SEE, WHERE THIS RIVER JOINS THE BIG RIVER...

THAT'S IT! THEY COULD GET OVER THE BORDER THAT WAY—AND WHAT'S THAT DRAWN UP UNDER THE CLIFFS? DUG-OUT CANOES!

THEY TAKE THE TRAIL AGAIN...

DIDN'T SEE ANY SIGN OF BREWSTER AND EVANS. THEY MIGHT BE HOLDING THEM HOSTAGE IN CASE OF TROUBLE — ONE OF 'EM'S WOUNDED ...HOW BADLY?

BWANA— THIS IS A RHINO-TRAIL! PERHAPS...

THE OLD GENTLEMAN HIMSELF! AND A SHOT WOULD BRING THE POACHERS DOWN ON US. WELL, I GUESS HE'S MORE SCARED THAN WE ARE...

NOT A SOUND, MIND—JUST BEHAVE LIKE LUNATICS! WITH ANY LUCK, HE'LL TURN TAIL...

AND HE HAS! PHEW — I THOUGHT HE'D GIVE US AWAY!

NOW THEN, ONA, HOW DO WE GET BWANA EVANS AND THE AMERICAN OUT OF THERE? ANY SUGGESTIONS?

THIS TASK I LOVE, BWANA. WE WAIT FOR NIGHT—THEN I CROSS THE WATER INTO THE CAMP!

TO BE CONTINUED

33

FRASER of AFRICA

Mystery surrounds the dis-appearance of a safari led by Hollywood star Jed Brewster. On its trail comes Fraser, with Hash, M'Kuki, and the Masai tracker, Ona. They find that Brewster and his White Hunter, Evans, have been overpowered by ivory-poachers. Ona suggests stealing into the poachers' camp by night, to rescue the two men . . .

FRANK BELLAMY.

BUT YOU'VE SWORN TO KILL THE AMERICANI BECAUSE HE SHAMED YOU, ONA!

ONLY LET ME DO THIS, BWANA, AND I PROMISE TO BRING HIM OUT ALIVE . . .

. . . MY REVENGE CAN WAIT!

VERY WELL, TONIGHT. MEANWHILE, WE MUSTN'T STIR, IN CASE THEY NOTICE US . . . CONFOUND IT— LOOK WHAT'S ARRIVED!

A FLOCK OF FLAMINGOES! YOU'LL HAVE TO GET THROUGH THEM TONIGHT, ONA.

THAT NIGHT, A GREY SHADOW STEALS OUT OF THE BUSH.

. . . PAST THE SLEEPING FLAMINGOES . . .

. . . AND INTO THE POACHERS' CAMP.

DOG OF A UKONO . . .

. . . DIE!

TO BE CONTINUED

FRASER of AFRICA

Mystery surrounds the disappearance of a safari led by Hollywood star Jed Brewster. On its trail comes Fraser, with Hash, M'Kuki, and the Masai tracker, Ona. They discover that Brewster and his White Hunter, Evans, have been overpowered by ivory-poachers. Ona steals into the poachers' camp by night, kills a guard, and . . .

NO, NO — HELP! HE-E-ELP!

SILENCE, BWANA EVANSI! I COME FROM YOUR FRIEND BWANA FRASER — I COME TO TAKE YOU AWAY.

A FEW MOMENTS LATER, ONE OF THE POACHERS, SCHAGEN, APPEARS IN THE HUT DOORWAY. . .

WHAT THE . . . ?

THE GUARD'S BEEN KILLED — STABBED! WHO'S BEEN HERE?

SOMEBODY FROM ACROSS THE WATER, OR THOSE FLAMINGOES WOULDN'T BE SO RESTLESS. MUST BE ONE OF EVANS'S NATIVE BOYS, FOLLOWING HIM.

DON'T SHOOT! I DON'T KNOW WHO IT WAS — I ONLY KNOW YOU'LL PAY FOR ALL THIS!

DON'T WORRY, MY FRIEND — YOU'RE IN TOO MUCH OF A FEVER TO ESCAPE. I'LL SET TWO GUARDS OVER YOU, TO MAKE SURE.

MEANWHILE, ONA REPORTS BACK TO FRASER. . .

ONLY BWANA EVANSI LIES HERE, BWANA — I DO NOT SEE THE AMERICANI. THEN THE LONG-BEARD COME AND . . .

SO BREWSTER'S MISSING! IT CAN ONLY MEAN ONE THING — HE'S DEAD!

TWO HOURS LATER, ONA SETS OFF ONCE MORE, THIS TIME WITH FRASER.

MARTIN FRASER!

MARTIN, THEY'VE KILLED BREWSTER — THEY'VE . . .

SAVE YOUR STRENGTH, BOB — WE'VE A LONG WAY TO GO!

TO BE CONCLUDED

35

The disappearance of a safari led by Hollywood star Jed Brewster has led to a search by Fraser, with Hash, M'Kuki, and the Masai tracker, Ona. Finding that Brewster has been murdered by ivory-poachers, Ona and Fraser rescue his friend Evans from their camp.

COME ON, YOU TWO! M'KUKI, YOU BRING UP THE REAR—WE'VE GOT TO GET THE BWANA EVANSI AWAY BEFORE THOSE BLACKGUARDS FIND OUT HE'S MISSING...

WE SHALL HAVE TO TRUST TO LUCK FOR A WAY OUT OF THIS CONFOUNDED RIFT.

BWANA! I HEAR SHOUTS. THEY FOLLOW US, I THINK.

FRANK BELLAMY

WATCH IT—TROUBLE!

THERE'S OUR OLD FRIEND OF YESTERDAY, TAKING HIS MUD-BATH. WONDER IF HE'LL ATTACK?

PHEW—HE'S LETTING US GO! BUT I CERTAINLY FEEL SORRY FOR ANYONE WHO TRIES TO FOLLOW. IN HIS PRESENT TEMPER, HE'LL MAKE HAY OF ANY FURTHER VISITORS.

AND THAT'S PRECISELY WHAT HAPPENS...

WE CAN'T AFFORD TO LET 'EM GO—THEY'LL WRECK THE WHOLE SET-UP!

DON'T FIRE! YOU'LL ONLY MANAGE TO WOUND HIM IN THIS LIGHT...

RUN FOR IT!

FURTHER ON, FRASER'S PARTY TAKES A REST...

OLD MAN RHINO HAS SAVED US—WE CAN AFFORD A BREATHER. THE BWANA EVANSI IS ALL IN.

THERE THEY GO WITH THEIR IVORY, SCOT FREE—FOR THE TIME BEING! BUT I PROMISE THEM THIS...

MORNING FINDS THEM SAFE BUT EXHAUSTED AT THE TOP OF THE PASS.

THERE'S GOING TO BE ONE ALMIGHTY OUTCRY WHEN THE WORLD LEARNS THAT JED BREWSTER'S DEAD! AS FOR THE POACHERS...

...I SWEAR BY ALL THE ELEPHANTS THEY'VE SLAIN, THAT I'LL SEE THEM IN THE DOCK BEFORE THEY'RE MUCH OLDER!

THE IVORY POACHERS – a gripping new Fraser of Africa adventure – gets off to a thrilling start in next week's EAGLE!

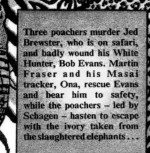

Three poachers murder Jed Brewster, who is on safari, and badly wound his White Hunter, Bob Evans. Martin Fraser and his Masai tracker, Ona, rescue Evans and bear him to safety, while the poachers — led by Schagen — hasten to escape with the ivory taken from the slaughtered elephants...

FOR HEAVEN'S SAKE, HURRY — WE DON'T KNOW HOW MANY MEN ARE UP THERE WATCHING US!

THEY WERE ENOUGH TO KILL TWO OF OUR SENTRIES AND GET EVANS AWAY.

THEN WHY DON'T THEY ATTACK US? MY GUESS IS THAT THERE'S ONLY ONE WHITE MAN UP THERE WITH HIS GUN-BEARER, SCHAGEN.

TO THE BOATS — GET ON WITH YOU!

ON THE HEIGHTS ABOVE...

MY SPEAR IS THIRSTY, BWANA FRASER!

I CAN'T LET 'EM GET AWAY WITH IT! ONA, YOU AND I ARE GOING TO STOP THOSE POACHERS.

BOB, I'LL GET THE TWO BOYS TO MAKE A LITTER AND CARRY YOU TO THE NEAREST POST — ONA AND I HAVE SOME BUSINESS TO ATTEND TO.

I'LL BE O.K., MARTIN — GET THOSE POACHERS, THAT'S ALL!

I'LL GET 'EM, ALL RIGHT!

THOSE ARE THEIR BOATS! THEY'LL FLOAT DOWN-RIVER TO UGALI AND GET CLEAN AWAY...

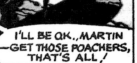

...BRING SOME DRY GRASS WITH YOU — WE'LL TRY TO SET FIRE TO THEIR BOATS!

CONFOUND IT — THE BOATS ARE TOO WET TO BURN!

BAD MEN COMING, BWANA!

FRANK BELLAMY

LET'S ARRANGE A FULL-SCALE RECEPTION-COMMITTEE FOR THEM. A COUPLE OF SHOTS AMONG THE HIPPO SHOULD START THINGS GOING...

GET BEHIND THOSE ROCKS, ONA — VERY SOON THINGS ARE GOING TO BE PRETTY LIVELY ROUND HERE!

TO BE CONTINUED

Fraser and his Masai tracker, Ona, are trying to stop three ivory poachers, led by Schagen, from getting away with the tusks of the elephants they have slaughtered. Fraser is outnumbered, so he enrages a herd of basking hippos by firing a couple of rifleshots among them . . .

FRANK BELLAMY

MUCH BETTER TO FIGHT THE POACHERS, BWANA!

THEY'RE TOO MUCH FOR US, ONA— LET THE HIPPOS DO OUR FIGHTING FOR US...

SCHAGEN, HENRI AND JOYCE REACH THEIR BOATS...

QUICK, NOW —LOAD UP!

WHAT'S GOT INTO THOSE HIPPOS

HIMMEL! CAN'T YOU HOLD THEM OFF UNTIL WE'VE LOADED?

SAVE YOUR BREATH, MON AMI, AND— FIRE!

A FOOTPRINT! SOMEONE WAS HERE, NOT FIVE MINUTES AGO.

FRASER'S RUSE HAS PROVED TOO MUCH FOR THE PORTERS...

CUT 'EM OFF, ONA—WE'RE GOING TO NEED THOSE PORTERS.

BACK—OR MY SPEAR SHALL TASTE YOUR HYENA'S BLOOD!

WHO'S AT THE BACK OF THIS?

A WHITE MAN!

A GAME-WARDEN, PERHAPS!

I KNOW YOU THREE— SCHAGEN, HENRI AND JOYCE—AND YOU NEEDN'T THINK YOU'RE GOING TO GET AWAY WITH THIS!

WE MIGHT HAVE GUESSED— IT'S FRASER!

A LONG SHOT, BUT...

SCHAGEN!

HELP, SCHAGEN— OR THE BRUTES WILL GET ME!

TO BE CONTINUED

Fraser and his Masai tracker, Ona, are trying to stop three ivory poachers, led by Schagen, from getting away with the tusks of the elephants they have slaughtered. Fraser is outnumbered, so he enrages a herd of basking hippos by firing a couple of shots . . .

MY HAT, IF I DON'T DO SOMETHING, THAT BLIGHTER WILL DROWN — AND I WANT THE THREE OF 'EM IN HANDCUFFS!

LEAVE THESE DOGS WITH ME, BWANA.

'LL NEVER MAKE IT — THE BRUTES WILL GO FOR ME, TOO...

SCHAGEN PUMPS BULLETS INTO THE FRANTIC HIPPOS...

...WHILE JOYCE HAULS THE HALF-DROWNED HENRI INTO HIS DUGOUT.

EVENTUALLY, THE THREE POACHERS GET CLEAR AWAY...

THEY'VE ESCAPED THIS TIME! THEY'LL FLOAT DOWN TO UGALI BEFORE I CAN GET WORD THROUGH. STILL, I'VE GOT THEIR TUSKS!

A FEW MINUTES LATER...

THIS MEANS THE LOCK-UP FOR ALL OF YOU, YOU KNOW THAT! CARRY THIS IVORY TO NYONGA...

...AND IT MAY HELP YOU WHEN YOU COME BEFORE THE DISTRICT COMMISSIONER.

FRANK BELLAMY

NYONGA, FIVE DAYS LATER...

IT'S FRASER! AND LOOK WHAT HE'S BROUGHT BACK WITH HIM...

WHILE FRASER TREATS HIMSELF TO THE LUXURY OF A HOT BATH...

..ONA STANDS GUARD OUTSIDE...

WHAT BLISS! WHAT BLISS!

HULLO — WHAT'S GOING ON OUT THERE?

TELL HIM IT'S THE DISTRICT COMMISSIONER!

ARE YOU THERE, FRASER? CALL OFF THIS MAN-EATER OF YOURS, WILL YOU?

TO BE CONTINUED

Fraser watches three poachers (Schagen, Henri and Joyce) escape down-river, but he manages to seize their ivory – the tusks of slaughtered elephants. Accompanied by Ona, the Masai, Fraser brings the ivory back to Nyonga. The District Commissioner calls on Fraser as he enjoys a much-needed bath . . .

FRANK BELLAMY

SORRY YOU SHOULD CATCH ME LIKE THIS, SIR.

YOU'VE EARNED YOUR BATH, FRASER. ARE YOU FIT ENOUGH TO SET OFF AGAIN RIGHT AWAY?

YOU KNOW THESE THREE POACHERS. WHERE ARE THEY LIKELY TO TURN UP NEXT?

THEN GET AFTER 'EM. TAKE ANYTHING YOU LIKE, ONLY – BRING 'EM IN!

HERE, SIR – AT THE LITTLE RIFT, ON THE KASU RIVER.

A WEEK LATER, FRASER IS 340 MILES AWAY WITH HIS TRACKER ONA, HIS GUN-BEARER, MKUKI, AND HIS COOK-BOY, HASH.

. . . THEY'VE LOST THEIR FEAR OF THE POACHERS.

THAT'S ODD! THE ELEPHANTS ARE ON THEIR WAY BACK TO THE LITTLE RIFT. IT CAN ONLY MEAN ONE THING . . .

LATER, FRASER ARRIVES AT THE LITTLE RIFT . . .

JUST LOOK AT ALL THAT GAME DOWN THERE — MAYBE I PICKED THE WRONG SPOT AFTER ALL!

I SUPPOSE THEY RECKON TO MAKE A QUICK GET-AWAY OVER THE BORDER . . .

WELL, WE'VE GOT TO GET THERE BEFORE THEY KILL ANY GAME!

BWANA! HO, BWANA!

IF THE POACHERS DON'T STRIKE HERE, ONA, WHERE WILL THEY STRIKE? AFRICA'S A BIG PLACE.

MESSAGE FROM NYONGA, BWANA. NATIVE BOY REPORT WHITE POACHERS HEADING FOR MULUNGU PLAINS.

MULUNGU! IT'S THE BEST PART OF 400 MILES WEST, OVER THE HILLS . . .

WHEN FRASER REACHES THE PLAINS . . .

I USED TO KNOW THE CHIEF OF THESE PARTS, AN OLD VILLAIN CALLED MUKUYUNI.

PUTTING HIS FOOT DOWN, FRASER HEADS FOR THE CHIEF'S VILLAGE AT TOP SPEED . . .

I SEE YOU, O MUKUYUNI. BUT WHAT EVIL AFFLICTS YOU THAT YOU WHITEN YOUR CHEEKS?

I SHOW THE BWANA!

YE GODS! IT'S ONE OF THE POACHERS — HENRI, IF I'M NOT MISTAKEN!

HE WILL BE DEAD BEFORE DAWN, BWANA!

TO BE CONTINUED

FRASER of AFRICA THE IVORY POACHERS

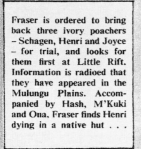

Fraser is ordered to bring back three ivory poachers – Schagen, Henri and Joyce – for trial, and looks for them first at Little Rift. Information is radioed that they have appeared in the Mulungu Plains. Accompanied by Hash, M'Kuki and Ona, Fraser finds Henri dying in a native hut . . .

NOT MUCH HOPE, I'M AFRAID. WHAT HAPPENED TO HIM, O CHIEF MUKUYUNI?

HE GO HUNT MAN-EATING LION, BWANA – INSTEAD, LION HUNT HIM!

WHY WERE THE THREE BWANAS HERE? WHICH WAY DID THEY GO?

MAN-EATER KILL MANY WOMEN, BWANA. YOU KILL HIM – I HELP YOU FIND BWANA S.

BEFORE SUNSET, FRASER SETS OUT LION-HUNTING, BUT ONA HAS IDEAS OF HIS OWN.

THIS LION BELONG ME, BWANA...

FOOTPRINTS, BWANA – A PIECE OF BLOODIED CLOTH. THE LION LEAP HERE!

WHY IS THIS LION YOURS, ONA?

BWANA KNOW I NEVER BEFORE KILL LION. NOW IS MY CHANCE TO BECOME A TRUE 'EL MORAN' – A WARRIOR.

ALL RIGHT – YOU STAY ON THAT SIDE OF THE STREAM AND I'LL STAY ON THIS, WITH THE BAIT IN BETWEEN...

HE WOULD NEVER FORGIVE ME IF I SHOT THE BEAST. ALL THE SAME, I'LL KEEP IT COVERED...

SO SILENCE FALLS, AND A LONG WAIT BEGINS...

THEN...

I SEE YOU, 'SIMBA'! MY SPEAR LONGS FOR YOUR HEART, AND MY SWORD IS HUNGRY FOR YOUR LIVER...

A SPLIT SECOND LATER, THE LION RUSHES AT ONA.

I WAS A FOOL TO AGREE TO THIS. ONA'S A MAN IN A THOUSAND, AND HE'LL BE LUCKY IF HE'S ONLY MAIMED...

...SHALL I FIRE?

FRANK BELLAMY

TO BE CONTINUED

Fraser, accompanied by M'Kuki, Hash and Ona, is ordered to bring back three ivory poachers for trial, and finds one of them dying in a native village. The local chief promises to help find the other poachers – Schagen and Joyce – if Fraser will kill the man-eating lion that mauled the mortally-injured poacher. Fraser's Masai tracker, Ona, insists on killing the lion single-handed . . .

YOUR DEATH COMES, O SIMBA — THUS!

I CAN'T LET THIS GO ON — I MUST GET IN NEARER, AND...

BUT ONA'S SWORD BUCKLES AGAINST THE MAN-EATER'S BREAST-BONE...

GRABBING HIS SPEAR ...

...ONA PLUNGES IT INTO HIS ENEMY.

KEEP AWAY — HE MAY NOT BE DEAD!

DOES THE BWANA TEACH A MASAI WHAT IS A DEAD LION AND WHAT IS A LIVE ONE?

THIS IS THE SONG OF ONA, THE KILLER OF LIONS, THE ONE-WHO-WALKS-BY-NIGHT, THE PEERLESS TRACKER, THE FEARED OF THE MIGHTY 'SIMBA'!

ONA SKINS OFF THE MANE.

I TAKE THE LION'S MANE TO SHOW THAT I HAVE BLOODED MY SPEAR IN 'SIMBA' — THE KING OF BEASTS!

NOW YOU'VE COOLED DOWN, ONA, LET'S GET BACK TO THE VILLAGE. THAT CHIEF IS HIDING SOMETHING, AND I'VE GOT TO GET TO THE BOTTOM OF IT...

THE LION IS DEAD — NOW TELL ME WHERE THE BAD MEN GO.

DOG — YOU LIE! I FOLLOW THEIR TRACKS YONDER, TO THE PLAINS.

INTO THE FOREST, BWANA.

WHY ARE THERE NO MEN OR BOYS IN YOUR VILLAGE, MUKUYUNI?

ANSWER!

BWANA — HO, BWANA!

ON THE OUTSKIRTS OF THE VILLAGE.

I FIND NEW SOIL ON THIS MOUND, BWANA — PERHAPS A NEW GRAVE!

WHAT LIES HERE?

TO BE CONTINUED

FRANK BELLAMY

Fraser is ordered to bring back three ivory poachers for trial and, accompanied by Hash, M'Kuki and Ona, finds one of them dying in a village. The local chief lies about the whereabouts of the others – Schagen and Joyce – until Fraser's gun-bearer, M'Kuki, discovers what looks like a grave . . .

I SHALL BE SHAMED FOR EVER IF I, MUKUYUNI, GREAT CHIEF OF THE ISOJO, AM MADE TO DIG.

DIG, CHIEF OF ALL HYENAS!

I THOUGHT SO – A HOARD OF TUSKS! TURN 'EM ALL OUT, YOU VILLAIN — A SCORE OR MORE OF ELEPHANTS HAVE DIED TO PROVIDE THIS IVORY.

NOW I SEE WHY YOUR VILLAGE IS EMPTY OF MEN—THEY HAVE JOINED THE POACHERS!

THE BWANA IS ALL-SEEING AND ALL-WISE, AND I AM A VERY OLD AND WEAK MAN. PITY ME!

SHOW ME WHICH WAY THE POACHERS WENT, AND PERHAPS I'LL SEE THAT YOU GET SIX MONTHS KNOCKED OFF YOUR SENTENCE!

I'LL TELL THE TRUTH TO THE MIGHTY FRASER, WHO IS AN EAGLE, AND MY MOTHER'S UNCLE...

SO, LATER THAT MORNING...

AND, THAT AFTERNOON...

IT'S THE DUST FROM SOME VEHICLE OR OTHER, AND MY BET IS THAT IT'S FRASER...

MUKUYUNI'S GIVEN US AWAY!

HE'LL MAKE CAMP, SOON, DAHIDA—RUN BACK AND FIND OUT HOW MANY THEY ARE!

FUNNY THING, ONA — I CAN'T HEAR ANY ANIMALS. WHAT'S SCARED THEM?

THE BWANA'S BED IS READY.

A FEW HOURS LATER...

THE WIND'S BLOWING STRAIGHT TOWARDS FRASER'S CAMP...

GRAB THE GUNS AND WATER, AND RUN FOR THE ROCKS!

FRASER SPRINGS OUT OF BED...

SMOKE! THE PLAINS ARE ON FIRE...

TO BE CONTINUED

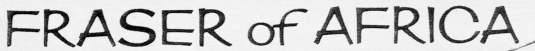

Fraser — accompanied by Ona, M'Kuki and Hash — is chasing two ivory poachers, Schagen and Joyce, who set fire to the long grass to dispose of their pursuers. Unknown to the poachers, Fraser and Co. escape death . . .

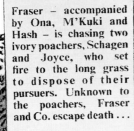

ALL SAFE?

ALL SAFE, BWANA—WE GO SEE WHAT IS LEFT OF OUR CAMP . . .

EVERYTHING GONE, BWANA. WHAT DO WE DO NOW?

MAKE USE OF THE FACT THAT SCHAGEN THINKS WE'RE ALL GONERS . . .

THE POACHERS THINK THEY'RE SAFE NOW, SO . . .

. . . WE'LL GO AFTER THEM . . .

HASH, DID YOU MANAGE TO SAVE THE WATER?

CANS BURST WITH THE HEAT, BWANA.

ONA POINTS OUT THE SPOT WHERE SCHAGEN STARTED THE FIRE . . .

SEE, BWANA— HERE WHERE FIRE WAS STARTED. HERE MEN'S FOOTPRINTS — THE WIND BLOW FIRE STRAIGHT TO OUR CAMP.

DAWN! THIS MUST BE THE NYOGI RIVER, AND WE'D BETTER KEEP OUT OF SIGHT — THE POACHERS CAN'T BE FAR OFF . . .

SOME TIME LATER . . .

THERE THEY ARE!

WE'LL MAKE THIS OUR HIDE-OUT. THOSE DEVILS WILL STOP AT NOTHING, AND WE MUST PLAN OUR NEXT MOVE CAREFULLY . . .

FRANK BELLAMY

HASH, YOU'D BETTER STAY HERE — ONA AND M'KUKI WILL COME WITH ME. WE'VE GOT TO FIND OUT WHAT THE POACHERS ARE UP TO.

WITH GREAT CARE, THE THREE MEN CRAWL FORWARD.

VERY BIG CAMP, MANY MEN, BWANA!

YES, M'KUKI, BUT IT LOOKS AS THOUGH THE WHITE BWANAS ARE GOING HUNTING. WE'LL HAVE TO SEIZE OUR OPPORTUNITY WHILE THEY ARE AWAY!

TO BE CONTINUED

Fraser – accompanied by Ona, M'Kuki and Hash – is hard on the heels of two ivory poachers, Schagen and Joyce, who believe that they have succeeded in killing their pursuers, by firing the long grass and burning Fraser's camp. Fraser, Ona and M'Kuki creep cautiously towards Schagen's camp . . .

THE LAST THING THAT THE POACHERS WILL EXPECT IS US ON THEIR TRAIL. WE CAN SURPRISE THEM, BUT...

SEE, BWANA! THE WHITE BWANAS MARCH TO THE RIVER...

THEY TAKE FOUR PORTERS, BWANA!

I SEE THE RACKS FOR DRYING MEAT, BWANA.

BUT WHERE ARE THE MEN?

SEE — SEE, BWANA!

THAT LEAVES TWELVE OR MORE OF MUKUYUNI'S MEN IN CAMP. NOW, HOW TO SCARE THEM AND...

BY GUM — I THINK I'VE GOT THE ANSWER!

FRANK BELLAMY

THEY DANCE BECAUSE THEY THINK THEY KILL THE MIGHTY FRASER!

AND BECAUSE OF THE PROSPECT OF A GREAT DEAL OF ELEPHANT MEAT...

FRASER, ONA AND M'KUKI MAKE FOR THE RIVER.

BUT THE MIGHTY FRASER ISN'T DEAD, BY A LONG CHALK — THOSE LADS ARE GOING TO GET THE SHOCK OF THEIR LIVES.

DAUB THIS WHITE CLAY OVER YOURSELVES. THEY SHALL HAVE THE PLEASURE OF *SEEING* THE MIGHTY FRASER AND HIS MEN DEAD — BUT STILL WALKING!

THIS IS NOT THE WAY OF A WARRIOR, BWANA — LET ME TAKE MY SWORD TO THEM.

I DON'T WANT 'EM DEAD, ONA — I WANT THEM IN CHAINS, AS AN EXAMPLE TO OTHER POACHERS.

THE DANCE OF VICTORY IS AT ITS HEIGHT, WHEN...

SEE! OH — THE WALKING SPIRITS!

TO BE CONTINUED

FRASER of AFRICA THE IVORY POACHERS

Fraser, Ona, M'Kuki and Hash are chasing two ivory poachers, Schagen and Joyce, to arrest them and their native accomplices. When Fraser and Co. escape death in a fire started by Schagen, they track down their unsuspecting quarry. After the poachers leave their camp to hunt, Fraser, Ona, and M'Kuki scare the remaining native 'boys' . . .

...BY PRETENDING TO BE GHOSTS...

THE GHOSTS THAT WALK !

IT IS BWANA FRASER, THE MIGHTY EAGLE, WHO WAS KILLED !

HE COMES TO AVENGE HIS DEATH ...A-A-A-AH!

THE DRUMMER STANDS PARALYSED WITH FEAR...

...BUT, SUDDENLY, WITH A SHRIEK...

EE, EEEH-EEH !

THAT MAY WRECK EVERYTHING – HE'LL TELL THE OTHERS THAT WE AREN'T GHOSTS AFTER ALL...

FIRST, LET'S RUB THIS CLAY OFF OURSELVES.

WE'VE GOT TO WORK QUICKLY. PILE ALL THEIR NECESSITIES ON TO THIS JEEP – GUNS, SLEEPING BAGS, AMMUNITION, MAPS, AND SO ON ...

A FEW MINUTES LATER ...

OFF YOU GO, M'KUKI – WE'LL CATCH UP WITH YOU.

COME WITH ME, ONA !

THIS BLAZE WILL PUT PAID TO EVERYTHING THE POACHERS HAVE GOT...

FRANK BELLAMY

FRASER AND ONA FINISH THEIR JOB AND JOIN M'KUKI...

THOSE BOYS OF SCHAGEN'S WILL DRIFT BACK TO THEIR VILLAGE, WHERE WE CAN PICK 'EM UP LATER. NOW TO GO AFTER THE POACHERS THEMSELVES.

WE DON'T WANT THIS EMPTY JEEP, AND WE CERTAINLY DON'T WANT THE POACHERS TO GET HOLD OF IT. I THINK IT'S TIME TO SEND IT ON ITS LAST JOURNEY !

TO BE CONTINUED

Fraser – accompanied by Ona, M'Kuki and Hash – is chasing two ivory poachers, Schagen and Joyce, who believe they have killed their pursuers. When the poachers have gone off to hunt, Fraser and Co. put their 'boys' to flight by pretending to be ghosts, burn the camp, and ride off in Schagen's jeep with all his equipment . . .

GET THE MOTOR GOING, M'KUKI– WE'LL SOON GET RID OF THIS SPARE JEEP. WE DON'T WANT IT TO FALL INTO SCHAGEN'S HANDS!

I DO IT, BWANA.

M'KUKI LETS IN THE CLUTCH AND JUMPS CLEAR.

THAT WILL GIVE THE LOCAL CROCS SOMETHING TO TALK ABOUT...

FRASER, ONA AND M'KUKI REJOIN HASH...

BWANA – YOU TAKE POACHERS' JEEP?

WE CERTAINLY HAVE, HASH! I'M LEAVING IT WITH YOU TO LOOK AFTER...

WE'VE GOT TO TRACK DOWN THOSE POACHERS BEFORE THEY DO TOO MUCH DAMAGE – LEAD THE WAY, ONA!

TWO POACHERS GO THIS WAY, BWANA. WITH THEM ARE TWO – THREE – FOUR BOYS.

WHY FOUR, I WONDER? THEY ONLY NEED TWO AS GUN-BEARERS. PERHAPS THE OTHER TWO ARE JUST RUNNERS...

ELEPHANT! NOW THAT'S A QUEER THING. IF THE POACHERS ARE AFTER IVORY, WHY DIDN'T THEY SLAUGHTER THEM?

FRANK BELLAMY

THEY'RE UP TO SOME SPECIAL DEVILMENT THIS TIME ...

AND I'VE GOT TO FIND OUT PRETTY QUICK WHAT IT IS...

BACK! I HEAR SOMEBODY COMING!

WA!

TWO OF SCHAGEN'S MEN. WE GIVE THEM BIG SURPRISE...

TO BE CONTINUED

Fraser – accompanied by Ona, M'Kuki and Hash – is chasing two ivory poachers, Schagen and Joyce. After seizing or destroying all their equipment, Fraser, Ona and M'Kuki track down their unsuspecting quarry. As they near their ruthless foes, Ona and M'Kuki leap on two of Schagen's 'boys' . . .

STAY WHERE YOU ARE, DOG!

BWANA, THESE MEN ARE RUNNING AWAY FROM THE POACHERS!

IT IS TRUE, O BWANA!

THE TWO WHITE BWANAS FORCE MY PEOPLE TO BURN THE PLAINS. THEY SHOOT WHEN WE SAY NO—SO WE TWO RUN AWAY.

WHAT'S THAT YOU SAID...

BURN THE PLAINS?

SO THAT'S THEIR PLAN—THEY'RE GOING TO TRAP ALL THE GAME THEY CAN IN A CIRCLE OF FIRE AND MASSACRE IT!

LEAD US TO YOUR VILLAGE!

ON REACHING THE BOYS' VILLAGE, FRASER AND CO. FIND THE INHABITANTS UP IN ARMS . . .

YOU'VE CERTAINLY GOT A NICE WELCOME LINED UP FOR US!

PUT YOUR SPEARS DOWN—THIS IS BWANA FRASER, WHO BRINGS THE LAW!

MY TWO BROTHERS, BWANA FRASER. THE WHITE BWANA WITH THE BEARD SHOOT THEM!

SCHAGEN! THAT DEVIL'S NOT GOING TO ESCAPE THIS TIME...

SEE—THE PLAINS ARE ON FIRE!

FRASER, ONA AND M'KUKI LEAVE THE VILLAGE AT ONCE.

FIRE'S SEVERAL MILES AWAY, I SHOULD JUDGE—SOMEWHERE NEAR THE AMALI CATARACTS...

MEANWHILE, JUST AS FRASER FEARS, THE GRASS IS BEING FIRED...

FRANK BELLAMY

...TO DRIVE THE GAME INTO A TRAP, WHERE IT CAN BE KILLED AT LEISURE BY SCHAGEN AND JOYCE.

HERE COMES THE FIRST, MY FRIEND—A BULL ELEPHANT!

NOW THAT WE'VE DISPOSED OF FRASER, WE CAN PICK THE COUNTRY CLEAN.

BUT FRASER IS VERY FAR FROM BEING 'DISPOSED OF'...

KEEP UP-RIVER, THEN WE SHALL OUTFLANK THOSE TWO MURDERERS...

...FOLLOW ME!

NOW THEN, LEAP THROUGH THE FLAMES AND...

TO BE CONTINUED

Fraser – accompanied by Ona, M'Kuki and Hash – is tracking down two ivory poachers, Schagen and Joyce, who believe that they have disposed of their pursuers. Just as Fraser, Ona and M'Kuki near their quarry, Schagen lights a wall of fire to trap the terrified game . . .

FRASER PLUNGES THROUGH THE BLAZING GRASS...

WE FOLLOW, O BWANA FRASER!

I SMELL BUFFALO.

I SMELL NOTHING BUT SMOKE!

GET BACK – AND LIE LOW.

I SPOKE TRUE – IT *IS* BUFFALO!

THEY RUN STRAIGHT INTO THE FLAMES...

CRAZED WITH FEAR – THEY'LL BE BACK.

SEE – THEY RUN BACK!

STRAIGHT INTO SCHAGEN'S RIFLE ...

THEY EMERGE FROM THE BURNING AREA...

THANK HEAVENS WE'RE OUT OF THE SMOKE!

BWANA – LOOK BWANA

THE TERRIFIED GAME RACES FROM THE FLAMES INTO THE NATURAL FUNNEL, OUT OF WHICH POUR THE AMALI CATARACTS.

SCHAGEN AND JOYCE WILL HAVE POSTED THEMSELVES ON THE ROCKS ACROSS THE RIVER...

WE'VE GOT TO GET BEHIND THEM – QUICKLY, BEFORE THEY START SHOOTING IN EARNEST!

FRANK BELLAMY

FROM NOW ON – NOT A SOUND!

THERE THEY ARE, BWANA!

WE LEAP ON THEM, BWANA?

SSSH! SOFTLY – LOOK BEHIND THEM...

...I THINK SOMEONE ELSE IS GOING TO DO OUR FIGHTING FOR US!

TO BE CONTINUED

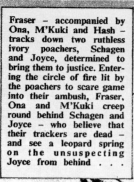

Fraser – accompanied by Ona, M'Kuki and Hash – tracks down two ruthless ivory poachers, Schagen and Joyce, determined to bring them to justice. Entering the circle of fire lit by the poachers to scare game into their ambush, Fraser, Ona and M'Kuki creep round behind Schagen and Joyce – who believe that their trackers are dead – and see a leopard spring on the unsuspecting Joyce from behind . . .

SCHAGEN! SHOOT, SHAGEN!

THROW DOWN YOUR RIFLE, SCHAGEN— THERE'S ONLY ONE OF YOU NOW TO OUR THREE!

FRASER!

YE GODS— SCHAGEN'S JUMPED FOR IT! HE'D SOONER FACE THE CATARACTS THAN ME...

HOLD YOUR FIRE, M'KUKI, AND GET AFTER HIM!

HE'S MADE IT — HE'S REACHED THE OTHER SIDE! QUICKLY!

STAY HERE, M'KUKI, WITH MY RIFLE, IN CASE SCHAGEN CIRCLES BACK. GIVE ME THE REVOLVER, AND DON'T HESITATE TO FIRE. ONA AND I WILL SWIM AFTER HIM—HE'S FOUR OR FIVE TIMES A MURDERER, AS WELL AS A POACHER.

FRASER AND ONA CROSS THE RIVER.

LUCKY FOR US HE'S CHOSEN TO RUN FOR IT, OR WE'D BE SITTING DUCKS AT THIS MOMENT.

AFTER HIM!

DON'T MOVE, ONA...

THEY PROBABLY WON'T BE ABLE TO SMELL US IN THIS SMOKE!

TO BE CONCLUDED

Fraser – accompanied by Ona, M'Kuki and Hash – has tracked down two ivory poachers, Schagen and Joyce, who light a wall of fire to trap the game. Joyce is killed by a leopard and Schagen makes a desperate run for it, with Fraser and Ona in hot pursuit . . .

THOSE ELEPHANTS ARE MORE SCARED THAN WE ARE, ONA, OR I WOULDN'T GIVE MUCH FOR OUR CHANCES AT THIS MOMENT...

BWANA — SEE!

WE'RE LOST! WHICH WAY WOULD SCHAGEN GO?

FOR AN INSTANT, THEY CATCH SIGHT OF SCHAGEN — WHO FIRES!

NOW WE'VE GOT HIM PROPERLY ON THE RUN!

SUDDENLY, FRASER REALIZES THAT ONA HAS BEEN HIT...

YOU'RE HURT!

THE SHOT TEAR MY LEG, BWANA — I CANNOT MOVE. I AM ASHAMED!

HERE GOES — I'LL G YOU OUT OF THI SOMEHOW

YOU SHOULD BE SAFE HERE, ONA, NOW I MUST GET AFTER SCHAGEN, BUT I'LL BE BACK.

BWANA NOT WORRY ABOUT ME — HURRY, HURRY!

A LONG AND EXHAUSTING CHASE FOLLOWS...

SCHAGEN'S MAKING FOR HIS CAMP. HE DOESN'T KNOW I DESTROYED IT AND SCATTERED HIS MEN — I'LL HAVE HIM THERE...

SCHAGEN IS HORRIFIED TO FIND EVERYTHING DESTROYED OR MISSING...

MY CAMP'S BURNED OUT — TRUCKS HAVE GONE — NOBODY HERE — I'M DONE!

NOT A MOVE, SCHAGEN, OR I FIRE! I'M TAKING YOU TO NYONGA TO STAND TRIAL FOR MURDER — UP ON YOUR FEET!

FRANK BELLAMY

Fraser takes Schagen to Nyonga, where the ruthless poacher is put on trial for his life, found guilty and executed. But the successful conclusion of one mission is only the signal for the start of another thrilling, dangerous exploit, as you will discover in next week's issue of EAGLE!

Leaving Ona, the Masai, to recover from his injuries in hospital, Fraser sets out on patrol in the Ngambi Game Reserve, together with M'Kuki, his gun-bearer, and Hash, the cook. As M'Kuki drives the Land Rover towards their H.Q. . . . .

REV UP YOUR ENGINE, M'KUKI — THAT GENERALLY MOVES 'EM !

FRANK BELLAMY

THERE THEY GO ! I REMEMBER THAT BLACK MALE — TWO YEARS AGO, HE ATTACKED A WOMAN...

BWANA !

A MAN !

WITH ALL THESE CATS ABOUT, HE'S TAKING A BIT OF A RISK...

I'VE GOT A FEELING THAT FELLOW IS UP TO SOMETHING, M'KUKI — YOU'D BETTER CALL UP THE DISTRICT COMMISSIONER'S OFFICE.

SO, AT NYONGA, ADMINISTRATIVE CENTRE OF THE NGAMBI DISTRICT...

THAT YOU, FRASER ? THE MAN YOU SAW WAS UNDOUBTEDLY M'BIMBA, THE MURDERER. REMEMBER THE CASE ? HE ESCAPED YESTERDAY FROM A ROAD GANG...

HE WAS CHIEF OF THE INSHIRRI, AND IS PROBABLY MAKING FOR HIS HOME ON THE KASU RIVER. M'BIMBA IS ALL TOGGED UP IN HIS CHIEF'S CLOBBER — AND THAT SPELLS TROUBLE — SO GET AFTER HIM, FRASER, AND REMEMBER...

...HE'S DANGEROUS !

RIGHT YOU ARE, SIR !

BWANA, LISTEN !

SOUNDS AS THOUGH THE LIONS HAVE TREED HIM...

THAT'S FINE — THEY'LL KEEP HIM NAILED DOWN UNTIL DAYLIGHT, WHEN WE CAN TAKE OVER.

BUT M'BIMBA HAS NO INTENTION OF WAITING FOR FRASER...

HE HAS URGENT BUSINESS ON THE KASU RIVER, WHICH CANNOT WAIT FOR LIONS OR FRASER.

TO BE CONTINUED

FRASER of AFRICA — THE SLAVERS

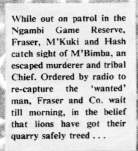

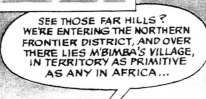

FRASER of AFRICA — THE SLAVERS

Accompanied by M'Kuki, Fraser is pursuing an escaped murderer called M'Bimba, formerly Chief of the Inshirri. Following clues which appear to have been deliberately left for him by M'Bimba, Fraser and M'Kuki make camp in the Northern Frontier District. When Fraser wakes, he finds that M'Bimba is towering over him...

DO NOT MOVE, M'BIMBA!

I ALSO KNOW THAT YOU LAY IN WAIT FOR ME, M'BIMBA! WAS IT TO KILL ME?

THE BWANA KNOWS THAT I WILL NOT HARM HIM.

LEAVE US, M'KUKI.

I WISH TO SPEAK ALONE WITH THE BWANA.

BUT THIS MAN IS A MURDERER...

ARE YOU GOING TO TELL ME THAT YOU DID NOT KILL THAT ARAB?

NOT SO, BWANA — I KILL HIM. I WISH NOW THAT I KILL HIS TWO BROTHERS, ALSO!

AM I NOT THE FATHER OF THE INSHIRRI? THESE THREE ARABS BRING DEATH TO MY PEOPLE. LET THE BWANA LISTEN TO MY STORY...

AFTER HEARING M'BIMBA'S STORY, FRASER DECIDES ON HIS NEXT MOVE...

STRIKE CAMP, M'KUKI — WE GO WITH THIS MAN TO HIS VILLAGE!

THIS I DO NOT UNDERSTAND, BWANA. HIS PEOPLE WILL KILL YOU!

IT'S A RISK I'VE GOT TO TAKE, M'KUKI. HE'S EITHER A HERO, OR THE BIGGEST LIAR IN ALL...

THE BWANA WILL SEE THAT I AM NO LIAR!

A long, foot-slogging journey begins towards the remote lands of the Inshirri, a river-people who dwell in the direction of Abyssinia. Soon, Fraser's belief in M'Bimba is justified by the turn of events...

HOLD BACK! WE DON'T WANT TO SCARE 'EM. THEY'VE GOT A NEW-BORN CALF THERE — SEE HOW THEY'RE GUARDING IT?

NOW I SHOW THE BWANA THAT I AM NO LIAR!

A LIONESS ALSO HAS HER EYE ON THE HELPLESS INFANT, AND FRASER'S SUDDEN APPEARANCE...

...ENRAGES THE ANIMAL...

FRANK BELLAMY

TO BE CONTINUED

Fraser, accompanied by M'Kuki, succeeds in tracking down an escaped murderer called M'Bimba. When he hears the 'wanted' man's story, however, Fraser agrees to go with Chief M'Bimba to his village, although M'Kuki is doubtful whether the man can be trusted. Suddenly, a savage lioness springs on Fraser...

M'KUKI DARE NOT SHOOT BUT, KNIFE IN HAND, M'BIMBA FLINGS HIMSELF ON THE LIONESS...

M'BIMBA SAVED MY LIFE! IS HE DEAD?

LIONESS STUN HIM, I THINK, BWANA.

HE'S COMING ROUND! GIVE ME SOME DRESSINGS, M'KUKI—THESE LACERATIONS ARE NOT DEEP, BUT WE MUST GUARD AGAINST BLOOD POISONING...

AFTER THIS, GREAT CHIEF OF THE INSHIRRI, I BELIEVE YOUR WORDS. TOMORROW, WHEN YOU ARE RESTED, WE GO TO YOUR VILLAGE.

WE GO NOW, BWANA —THERE IS NO TIME FOR REST!

SO THE LONG TREK CONTINUES UNTIL EVENING...

BWANA FRASER, YOU HAVE NOT EXPLAINED WHY WE GO WITH THIS MAN WHEN THE BWANA WAS ORDERED TO TAKE HIM BACK TO PRISON.

IT'S AN INCREDIBLE STORY, M'KUKI—ALL BOUND UP WITH THE ONE WORD...

...SLAVERS! HE SAYS THAT THE ARAB WHOM HE KILLED WAS A SLAVER, AND THAT TWO OTHER ARABS HAVE SINCE ROUNDED UP THE INSHIRRI AND DRIVEN THEM OFF.

WHY DID HE NOT SAY THIS AT HIS TRIAL?

BECAUSE THE ARABS PROMISED TO LEAVE HIS PEOPLE ALONE IF HE KEPT SILENT—THEY BROKE THEIR WORD! NOW SLEEP...

NEXT DAY...

HO, BWANA!

LOOK AT THAT! A HUMAN SKELETON WITH A SLAVE-RING ROUND ITS NECK—AND EVERYBODY THOUGHT SLAVERY HAD BEEN STAMPED OUT FORTY YEARS AGO!

FRANK BELLAMY

TO BE CONTINUED

FRASER of AFRICA

Fraser and M'Kuki track down an escaped convict called M'Bimba, a chief whose people have been carried off by Arab slavers. M'Bimba explains that he only killed one of the Arabs because the man broke his promise to let the Inshirri alone. As the three men approach M'Bimba's village, Fraser finds evidence to support the chief's story . . .

ARE THERE ANY MORE SKELETONS DOWN THERE, M'BIMBA? THIS POOR SOUL WAS A SLAVE RIGHT ENOUGH— THERE'S THE SLAVE-RING ROUND THE NECK...

I COUNT FOUR, FIVE, SIX SKELETONS, BWANA—PERHAPS MORE DOWN THERE.

ANY TRACE OF WHAT TRIBE THEY BELONGED TO?

A WOMAN'S COMB, BWANA— NOTHING ELSE. ALL THOSE SKELETONS BELONG WOMEN — THEY NOT MY PEOPLE, BWANA...

WOMEN! I SUPPOSE THE SLAVERS FOUND THEM USELESS, AND THREW THEM DOWN THERE. I SHOULD JUDGE IT HAPPENED SOME TIME AGO...

...WELL, M'BIMBA, ALL YOU SAY IS ONLY TOO TRUE — LET'S GET AFTER THOSE SWINE!

THAT AFTERNOON...

BWANA—MY PEOPLE LIVE AMONG THOSE ROCKS, YOU SEE? THEY FISH, THEY GROW MAIZE, THEY VERY HAPPY...

NOW I KNOW MY PEOPLE ARE DRIVEN AWAY. THOSE ELEPHANTS BATHE NEAR WHERE OUR NETS DRY, AND THEY TRAMPLE DOWN OUR PLANTATIONS...

YOU SMELL BURNING, BWANA?

FRANK BELLAMY

THEY REACH WHAT IS LEFT OF M'BIMBA'S VILLAGE.

LET ME WEEP, BWANA. MY FATHER MADE OF THE INSHIRRI ONE PEOPLE — NOW THEY ARE SLAVES, AND THEIR HOME IS DESTROYED!

PERHAPS SOME ARE STILL ALIVE, M'BIMBA—LET'S SEARCH THE VILLAGE...

DIDN'T I HEAR A MOVEMENT INSIDE THERE?

FATHER!

TO BE CONTINUED

Fraser and M'Kuki track down an escaped convict called M'Bimba, a chief whose people have been carried off by Arab slavers. M'Bimba explains that he only killed one of the Arabs because he broke his promise to let the Inshirri alone. They find M'Bimba's village destroyed and deserted, except for one man . . .

THIS IS MY FATHER, BWANA—THE GREAT MALINDI, ONCE CHIEF OF THE INSHIRRI. NOW SEE HIM!

LAY ME IN THE SUN, M'BIMBA. THE ARABS LEFT ME TO DIE BECAUSE I AM OLD AND WEAK, BUT I LIVE BECAUSE I KNEW THAT YOU WOULD COME . . .

NOW I DIE, KNOWING THAT YOU WILL AVENGE ME AND YOUR PEOPLE. DO YOU SWEAR IT, M'BIMBA?

I SWEAR IT, MALINDI— I WILL SLAY THESE MEN AND BRING MY PEOPLE BACK!

THERE'S JUST ONE THING, M'BIMBA. YOU ARE A MURDERER, AND MY DUTY IS TO TAKE YOU BACK TO PRISON . . .

THE BWANA IS A MAN AMONG MEN!

. . . BUT I'M GOING TO RISK MY JOB BY COMING WITH YOU!

LATER . . .
THE QUESTION IS, IN WHICH DIRECTION DID THEY DRIVE YOUR PEOPLE, M'BIMBA?

THEY GO BY WATER, BWANA—THERE IS NO OTHER TRAIL, AND THE BOATS ARE GONE . . .

THEY BURN OR STEAL ALL OUR BOATS, BUT THEY DO NOT FIND THIS ONE.

AND WOULD THEY GO UP-RIVER OR DOWN?

LET'S TOSS FOR IT —HEADS FOR UP-RIVER, TOWARDS ABYSSINIA, TAILS FOR DOWN-RIVER . . .

HEADS IT IS!

HIM VERY HARD WORK AGAINST THE CURRENT!

THESE MUST BE THE KULAI FALLS! THEY COULDN'T HAVE CLIMBED THEM . . .

I WAS WRONG, AND WE MUST TURN BACK DOWN-RIVER.

HIM VERY MUCH EASIER THIS WAY, BWANA.

YES, BUT IT'S THE BEST PART OF A DAY LOST, M'BIMBA.

HO, BWANA!

TO BE CONTINUED

Fraser, with the faithful M'Kuki and M'Bimba, the escaped convict, find M'Bimba's village destroyed and its people driven into slavery by Arabs. M'Bimba swears that he will follow and free them, and Fraser promises to help him. They quickly set off in pursuit by river . . .

WE SHALL HAVE TO CARRY THE BOAT ACROSS THE SHALLOWS, BWANA.

YES, AND SMACK THROUGH THAT INTERESTED AUDIENCE OF OUTSIZE SUNBATHERS!

BOAT HIM TOUCH ROCKS, BWANA.

ALL RIGHT—YOU TWO GET THE DUG-OUT ACROSS, WHILE I TRY TO SCARE THE HIPPOS OFF...

A COUPLE OF SHOTS IN THE AIR SHOULD DO THE TRICK...

INTO THE BUSH, THANK GOODNESS!

BUT ONE BULL HIPPO IS NOT SO EASILY FRIGHTENED...

BWANA! RUN-RUN, BWANA!

FRASER AND CO. RESUME THEIR JOURNEY...

YOU LOST YOUR WAR-SPEAR, M'BIMBA—BUT AT LEAST IT WAS IN A JOLLY GOOD CAUSE!

LATER...

SOON WE MAKE CAMP, BWANA?

I CATCH FISH —YOU MAKE FIRE!

RIGHT—LET'S TRY THAT SANDBAR...

WHAT IS IT, M'KUKI?

BEHIND THE BWANA —ON THE BANK! BWANA NOT MOVE SUDDENLY.

I SEE WHAT YOU MEAN— THEY PROBABLY THINK WE'RE SLAVERS!

TO BE CONTINUED

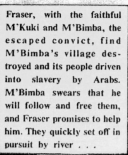

Fraser, accompanied by Chief M'Bimba and the faithful M'Kuki, is pursuing some Arab slavers who have driven off M'Bimba's people, the Inshirri. Suddenly, just as Fraser and Co have stopped for food on a sandbar, up in the Northern Frontier District of Kenya . . .

DON'T MOVE. — THOSE ARROWS WILL BE POISONED!

THOSE PEOPLE SAVAGES, BWANA — I UNDERSTAND NOTHING.

CAN YOU UNDERSTAND WHAT THEY'RE SHOUTING, M'BIMBA?

WELL, THEY OBVIOUSLY WANT SOMETHING...

I GO SPEAK, BWANA! THEY KILL YOU, BECAUSE THEY THINK YOU MAKE THEM SLAVES...

THROW YOUR GUN DOWN, M'KUKI — AT LEAST WE'LL TRY TO SHOW THEM THAT WE ARE FRIENDLY.

YE GODS, THEY'RE TAKING HIM AWAY! WE'VE GOT TO GET AFTER 'EM AND...

YOU HEAR THOSE DRUMS, BWANA?

I BELIEVE THEY MEAN TO SACRIFICE M'BIMBA AND MAKE A MEAL OF HIM...

STOP, M'KUKI! THEY'LL EXPECT US TO FOLLOW — THEY MAY EVEN HAVE SET A TRAP FOR US — SO WE MUST GET BACK AND THINK OF SOMETHING ELSE...

YOU CAN JUST SEE WHERE THE RIVER MAKES AN ELBOW, M'KUKI — THEIR VILLAGE MUST BE IN THE CROOK SOMEWHERE.

MOORING THE BOAT, FRASER AND M'KUKI STEALTHILY CREEP TOWARDS THE VILLAGE WHERE M'BIMBA IS HELD PRISONER...

WHAT DO YOU PLAN TO DO THEN, BWANA?

GET BACK TO THE BOAT, QUICK, AND SEE IF WE CAN APPROACH THE VILLAGE UNOBSERVED BY WATER.

KEEP YOUR FINGERS CROSSED, M'KUKI, AND HOPE THEY WON'T EXPECT US TO MAKE USE OF THE BACK DOOR!

TO BE CONTINUED

FRASER of AFRICA

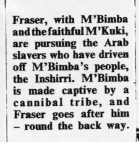

Fraser, with M'Bimba and the faithful M'Kuki, are pursuing the Arab slavers who have driven off M'Bimba's people, the Inshirri. M'Bimba is made captive by a cannibal tribe, and Fraser goes after him – round the back way.

THERE IS THE JU-JU HUT, BWANA. VILLAGE BOYS NOT GO NEAR IT.

ALL THE SAME, SOMEBODY'S INSIDE THERE, M'KUKI!

HIM WITCH-DOCTOR, BWANA.

I'M GOING TO GRAB HIM! READY?

FOR HEAVEN'S SAKE KEEP THAT OLD FRAUD QUIET...

...WHILE I TAKE A LOOK INSIDE THIS HUT...

M'BIMBA! THIS IS BWANA FRASER...

FRASER CUTS M'BIMBA FREE.

THIS IS WHERE WE HURRY, M'BIMBA!

ANYONE IN SIGHT, M'KUKI?

ALL CLEAR, BWANA.

TO THE BOAT, LADS...

WE MUST GET AWAY FROM HERE FAST!

MADE IT! AND THOSE BLACK CANNIBALS CAN GO HUNGRY.

THE NEXT DAY, THE ADVENTURERS ENTER A REGION OF MUD AND REEDS.

WE GET LOST SOON, BWANA.

WHICH WAY THE SLAVERS TAKE MY PEOPLE?

PULL OVER THERE. IT LOOKS LIKE A LANDING PLACE.

A TRAIL, BWANA! ONE-TWO-THREE MEN COME THIS WAY. THEY FALL—THEY GO ON—WA!

BWANA!

TO BE CONTINUED

Fraser, with M'Bimba and the faithful M'Kuki, are pursuing Arab slavers who have driven off M'Bimba's people, the Inshirri. Soon after rescuing M'Bimba from a cannibal tribe, they enter a region of mud and reeds. There, they find three emaciated Inshirri tribesmen, lying exhausted behind a tree . . .

THEY BELONG INSHIRRI, BWANA. THEY GO HUNGRY LONG TIME, I THINK.

POOR WRETCHES! LET'S GET THEM TO THE RIVER-BANK AND GIVE THEM SOME FOOD.

SO FRASER AND HIS FRIENDS HELP THE TWO TRIBESMEN BACK TO THE RIVER . . .

ARE THEY STRONG ENOUGH TO TALK, M'BIMBA?

THEY ESCAPED BWANA, AND GOT LOST. THEY LIE DOWN TO DIE — THEN WE FIND THEM.

ASK THEM WHERE THE ARABS WERE LEADING THE OTHER POOR SLAVES, M'BIMBA?

THEY SAY TO THE DIAMOND-MINES, BWANA.

WHAT ON EARTH DO THEY MEAN? THERE ARE NO DIAMOND-MINES UP HERE...

OR ARE THERE?

FRASER AND M'BIMBA SURVEY THE SURROUNDING TERRITORY.

THEY SAY THAT WAY GO TO UGALI, BWANA! ARABS TAKE SLAVES THE OTHER WAY.

I SEE! AND DO THEY KNOW WHERE IT LEADS TO?

HIM BIG BIG WATER, BWANA.

H'MMM! AND THEY OVERHEARD THE ARABS TALK OF DIAMONDS. WELL, I'VE NEVER BEEN THERE, SO...

TELL THESE MEN OF YOURS, M'BIMBA, NOT TO WORRY ABOUT THE ARABS ANY MORE, BUT TO GET BACK HOME...

NOW WE'LL GO AFTER THOSE SLAVES!

WHAT ELSE DID YOU TELL THEM?

I FREE MY PEOPLE, THE INSHIRRI, AND BRING THEM HOME TO LIVE IN PEACE.

THE TRAIL GETS WARM, AS FRASER AND CO. PRESS ON AT TOP SPEED.

THE CURRENT'S BEGINNING TO TAKE US ALREADY. WE SHALL LOSE CONTROL IN A MINUTE...

PULL IN OVER THERE!

FRANK BELLAMY

MANY PEOPLE COME HERE BEFORE US, BWANA. BOATS COME, MEN PULL THEM FROM WATER, SEE? THEY CARRY THEM INTO TREES—NOT LONG AGO, I THINK.

YOU HEAR A NOISE, BWANA?

RUSHING WATER! THE ARABS FORCED THEIR PRISONERS TO MAKE A PORTAGE ROUND CATARACTS...

WE LOSE MUCH TIME WALKING AFTER THEM, BWANA.

BUT THE BWANA DARE NOT...

DAREN'T HE? WHEN THE BWANA WAS FIFTEEN, HE TOOK A BOAT DOWN THE FINDHORN. NOW THAT REALLY IS A RIVER!

TO BE CONTINUED

Fraser, with M'Bimba and M'Kuki, are pursuing the Arab slavers who have driven off M'Bimba's people, the Inshirri. Fraser risks taking his frail boat down the cataracts, in order to get one jump ahead of the caravan of captive natives . . .

'YE WATERS — *HO!* I RIDE YOU LIKE A MASTER FOR I AM M'BIMBA, FATHER OF THE INSHIRRI, THE TAMER OF RIVERS — *HO!'*

M'BIMBA SINGS IN TRIUMPH . . .

. . . BUT RATHER TOO SOON!

I SAVE YOU, BWANA!

YOUR RIFLE, M'KUKI — HOLD OUT YOUR RIFLE!

THAT WAS A CLOSE SHAVE!

FRASER AND CO. TAKE STOCK OF THEIR SITUATION . . .

WHAT HAVE WE LEFT TO HELP US AGAINST THE SLAVERS?

MY RIFLE IS UNDAMAGED, BWANA — I CLEAN IT.

WE ALSO HAVE OUR LIVES, BWANA.

A FEW MINUTES LATER . . .

BWANA! I HEAR WAILING. MY PEOPLE COME — THE INSHIRRI — IT IS THEIR SONG . . .

THERE THEY ARE — COMING OVER THE HILL!

SO WE *HAVE* BEATEN THEM TO IT!

LET THE BWANA LISTEN TO MY PLAN . . .

THIS CALLS FOR SOME QUICK THINKING. HOW ARE WE TO TACKLE THEM, M'BIMBA?

FRANK BELLAMY

FIRST WE WIPE OUT OUR FOOTPRINTS — LIKE THIS . . .

THEY COME DOWN THIS PATH — I GO THIS SIDE, YOU GO THAT.

RIGHT! MEN CALL YOUR TRIBE FISH-EATERS, M'BIMBA, BUT I SEE THAT YOU ARE TRULY WARRIORS . . .

TO BE CONCLUDED

FRASER of AFRICA  THE SLAVERS